Physics
for CCEA
AS Level | Revision Guide

COLOURPOINT EDUCATIONAL

Pat Carson and Roy White

© Roy White, Pat Carson and Colourpoint Books 2012

ISBN: 978 1 78073 018 9

First Edition
Second Impression

Layout and design: April Sky Design, Newtownards
Printed by: GPS Colour Graphics Ltd, Belfast

Colourpoint Educational
An imprint of Colourpoint Creative Ltd
Colourpoint House
Jubilee Business Park
21 Jubilee Road
Newtownards
County Down
Northern Ireland
BT23 4YH

Tel: 028 9182 6339
Fax: 028 9182 1900
E-mail: info@colourpoint.co.uk
Web site: www.colourpoint.co.uk

The Authors

Roy White has been teaching Physics to A-level for over 30 years in Belfast. He is currently Head of Department and an enthusiastic classroom practitioner. In addition to this text, he has been the author or co-author of three successful books supporting the work of science teachers in Northern Ireland.

Pat Carson has been teaching Physics to A level for over 30 years in Belfast and Londonderry. He is currently Vice-Principal in a Londonderry Grammar school.

The authors co-wrote Colourpoint's successful A-level textbooks *Physics for CCEA AS Level* and *Physics for CCEA A2 Level*.

Important Note to Students

This guide has been written to help students preparing for the AS Physics specification from CCEA. While Colourpoint Creative Ltd and the authors have taken every care in its production, we are not able to guarantee that the book is completely error-free. Additionally, while the book has been written to closely match the CCEA specification, it the responsibility of each candidate to satisfy themselves that they have fully met the requirements of the CCEA specification prior to sitting an exam set by that body. For this reason, and because specifications change with time, we strongly advise every candidate to avail of a qualified teacher and to check the contents of the most recent specification for themselves prior to the exam. Colourpoint Creative Ltd therefore cannot be held responsible for any errors or omissions in this book or any consequences thereof.

Copyright of Past Paper Questions

The past paper questions in this book have been reproduced with permission of CCEA. CCEA GCE Sciences Compendium 2006-2011. ©CCEA with the permission of the Northern Ireland Council for the Curriculum, Examinations and Assessment.

Contents

Unit AS 1:
Forces, Energy and Electricity

1.1 Physical Quantities

Students should be able to:

1.1.1 describe all physical quantities as consisting of a numerical magnitude and unit;

1.1.2 state the base units of mass, length, time, current, temperature, amount of substance and be able to express other quantities in terms of these units;

Physical Quantities

To describe a physical quantity we first define a characteristic unit. To state a measurement of a physical quantity, such as force, we need to state two things:

1. A **magnitude** (a numerical value) and

2. A **unit**.

International System of Units (SI units)

The SI system of units defines seven base quantities from which all other units are derived. The table below shows the **six base quantities and the units in which they are measured**.

Quantity	Unit	Symbol
mass	kilogram	kg
time	second	s
length	metre	m
electric current	ampere	A
temperature	kelvin	K
amount of substance	mole	mol

Multiples and submultiples of these base units are commonly used:

Prefix	Factor	Symbol
pico	10^{-12}	p
nano	10^{-9}	n
micro	10^{-6}	μ
milli	10^{-3}	m
centi	10^{-2}	c
kilo	10^{3}	k
Mega	10^{6}	M
Giga	10^{9}	G
Tera	10^{12}	T

Derived Units

Many SI units are **derived**. They are defined in terms of two or more base units. For example velocity, in metres per second, which is written as ms^{-1}. You must be able to write a physical quantity in terms of its base units.

Worked Example

The derived unit for energy is the joule. What are the base units of energy?

To calculate the base units for energy we can use any valid formula for energy such as that below for kinetic energy, E_k:

$E_k = \frac{1}{2}mv^2$ (the ½ being a number has no units)

unit for energy = unit for mass × unit for velocity × unit for velocity

$= kg \times ms^{-1} \times ms^{-1}$

$= kg\, m^2\, s^{-2}$ which gives the joule **in terms of base units only**.

Exercise 1

1. The pascal, the coulomb, the watt, the volt and the ohm are all S.I. units, but they are not S.I. base units. Express each of these units in terms of S.I. base units. (CCEA June 2010 amended)

2. The list below gives a number of physical quantities and units. Circle those which are **base** quantities or **base**

   units:
   Coulomb, Force, Length, Mole, Newton, Temperature
   (CCEA January 2009)

3. The energy, E, of a photon of wavelength, l, is given by the equation $E = hc/\lambda$, where c is the speed of light. Find the SI base units in which h is measured.

1.2 Scalars and Vectors

Students should be able to:

1.2.1 distinguish between and give examples of scalar and vector quantities;

1.2.2 calculate the resultant of two coplanar vectors by calculation or scale drawing, with calculations limited to two perpendicular vectors;

1.2.3 resolve a vector into two perpendicular components;

Distinguishing Scalars and Vectors

A **vector** is a physical quantity that needs magnitude, a **unit** and a **direction**.

A **scalar** is a physical quantity that requires only magnitude and a unit.

Here is a table of some of the more common vectors and scalars:

Vector	Scalar
Displacement	Distance
Velocity	Speed
Acceleration	Rate of change of speed
Force	Mass
Electric current	Electric charge
Momentum	Kinetic energy
	Temperature
	Area
	Volume
	Time

Combining Coplanar Vectors

When we add vectors we have to take into account their direction as well as their magnitude. When we add two or more vectors, the final vector is called the **resultant**. For two forces of 15 N and 10 N acting in the **same direction**, the resultant is 25 N. For two forces of 15 N and 10 N acting in opposite directions, the resultant is 5 N in the direction of the larger force.

Adding and Subtracting Vectors

If the vectors are not in a straight line then we use the **nose to tail** method to find the resultant. In the diagram below the resultant of the two vectors, A and B, is C. **C = A + B**

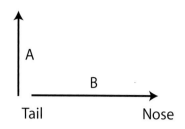

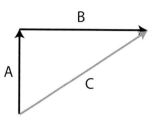

The resultant of subtracting the vector B from A is another vector D. The vector **−B** is a vector of the **same magnitude as B** but in the **opposite direction**. Effectively we add the negative vector so **D = A + (−B)**

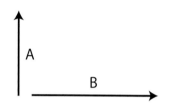

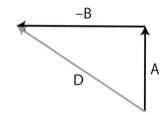

By drawing the vectors to scale and adding them in pairs we can find the resultant of any number of vectors, provided we know their magnitude and direction. This method can be used even if the vectors are not at right angles.

Worked Example

Look at the diagram. Linda moved 3.0 m to the east (AB) and then 4.0 m to the north (BC). Find the magnitude and direction of the resultant.

$AC^2 = AB^2 + BC^2 = 3^2 + 4^2 = 25$

$AC = \sqrt{25} = 5.0$

Although she has moved a total distance of 7.0 m, her displacement is **5.0 m** (AC) from the start. Since displacement is a vector, a magnitude and a direction are both needed.

$\tan \theta = $ opposite ÷ adjacent $= 4 \div 3 = 1.333$

giving   **θ = 53.13°**

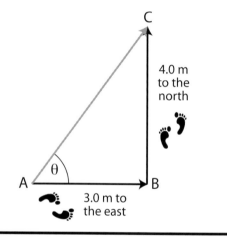

Components of a Vector

It is often useful to split or **resolve** a vector into two parts or components. The diagram shows a vector F that has been resolved into two components that are at right angles to each other.

$\sin \phi = $ opp ÷ hyp $= F_y \div F$ so, **$F_y = F \sin \phi$**

$\cos \phi = $ adj ÷ hyp $= F_x \div F$ so, **$F_x = F \cos \phi$**

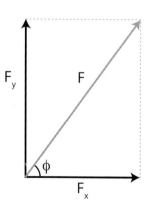

The Inclined Plane

Consider a mass, m, on a plane inclined at angle θ to the horizontal. Its weight, mg, acts vertically downwards as in Diagram A. The component of the weight parallel to the plane is mg sinq as in Diagram B. The normal reaction to the plane is equal to the component of the weight perpendicular to the plane (N = mg cosθ) as in Diagram C.

Diagram A	Diagram B	Diagram C

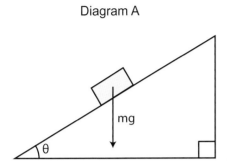

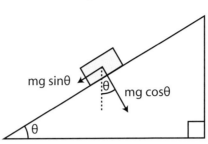

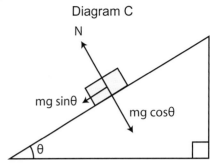

Worked Example

A man, pushing a wheelbarrow and load of total mass 22 kg, approaches a slope inclined at 5.0° to the horizontal, as shown in the diagram. Calculate the total force the man must exert on the wheelbarrow and its contents to move it up the slope at a constant speed of 1.5 m s⁻¹. The frictional force is constant at 12 N.

(CCEA January 2009, amended)

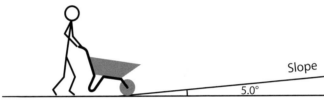

The constant speed means there is no resultant force. Both friction and the component of the weight parallel to the plane act down the slope. The man must therefore exert a force of equal size up the slope.

Force required = Friction + Component of weight parallel to plane

$$= 12 + 22 \times 9.81 \times \sin 5° = 30.8 \text{ N} \approx 31 \text{ N}$$

Equilibrium of Forces

If the resultant force on an object is zero then it is in **translational equilibrium.** Consider the worked example below.

Worked Example

Two tugs are used to rescue a small ship which has lost engine power and is close to some rocks. The tugs just manage to hold the ship stationary against a current producing a force of 250 kN on the ship. Tug A develops a force of 200 kN in the direction shown on the diagram. Find the magnitude and direction θ of the force F developed by tug B if the three forces acting on the ship are in equilibrium. (CCEA legacy June 2009, amended)

Since the forces are in equilibrium the vertical components of the forces balance and the horizontal components also balance.

Vertical: **F sin θ** = 200 sin 35 = 115 kN

Horizontal: F cos θ + 200 cos 35 = 250 kN

so **F cos θ** = 86 kN

Dividing the equations in bold type gives:

$$\tan θ = 115 \div 86$$

so $θ = \tan^{-1}(115 \div 86) = 53°$

Substituting for θ gives:

$$F = 86 \div \cos 53° = 143 \text{ kN}$$

So, F = 143 kN at 53° to the horizontal.

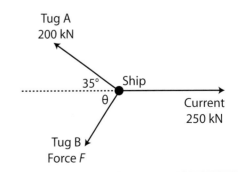

Exercise 2

1. The following is a list of physical quantities.
   Energy, Force, Temperature, Acceleration, Distance
   (i) Underline those that are vectors.
   (ii) State the difference between a vector and a scalar.
   (CCEA January 2010)

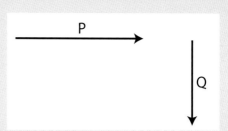

2. The diagram shows a force of 12 N acting on a brick resting on a horizontal surface.
   (i) Find by calculation the horizontal and vertical components of this force.
   (ii) What is the resultant vertical force acting on the horizontal surface if the brick has mass 3.0 kg?
   (CCEA January 2011)

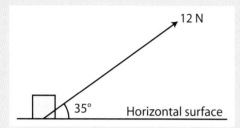

3. The diagram shows two vectors P and Q. Sketch the constructions necessary to obtain the vectors A and B, where A = P + Q and B = P − Q.
   (Drawings to scale are not required.)
   (CCEA January 2009)

4. The diagram shows two children playing by pulling on a rope connected through a smooth hook on a beam. Child A pulls with a force of 210 N at an angle of 55° from the horizontal.

   (i) Calculate the vertical component of the force with which child A is pulling.
   When child B pulls on the rope with a force of 128 N at 20° above the horizontal, the rope does not move.
   (ii) What condition must be met for this to happen?
   (iii) Confirm, by calculation, that the forces given satisfy this condition.
   (CCEA January 2010 amended)

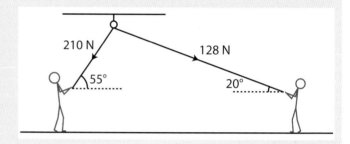

1.3 Linear Motion

Students should be able to:

1.3.1 define displacement, speed, velocity and acceleration;

1.3.2 recall and use the equations of motion for uniform acceleration;

1.3.3 describe an experiment to measure acceleration of free fall, g; and

1.3.4 interpret velocity-time and displacement-time graphs for motion with uniform and non-uniform acceleration.

Definitions

Displacement is the distance moved in a particular direction.

Speed is defined as the distance moved per second.

Velocity is defined as the displacement per second.

Average velocity is defined by the equation: $\text{Average velocity} = \dfrac{\text{Total displacement}}{\text{Total time taken}}$

Acceleration is defined as the rate of change of velocity with time.

Equations of Motion for Uniform Acceleration

Below are four equations which students need to remember and be able to use.

$$v = u + at$$
$$s = \tfrac{1}{2}(u + v)t$$
$$s = ut + \tfrac{1}{2}at^2$$
$$v^2 = u^2 + 2as$$

where:
u = initial velocity
v = final velocity
a = constant acceleration
t = time taken
s - displacement

Worked Example

Competitor A in a cycle race reaches a point 60.0 m from the finishing line. He then travels with uniform velocity of 18.0 ms⁻¹ in a straight line towards the finish. Another competitor B reaches the same point 60.0 m from the finish 0.100 s after A, travelling with the same velocity (18.0 ms⁻¹) as A. However, B then accelerates uniformly at 0.720 ms⁻² until he reaches the finish.

(a) Calculate the velocity with which competitor B crosses the finishing line.

(b) Make appropriate calculations to determine which competitor wins the race.

(a) $u = 18.0 \text{ ms}^{-1}$ $a = 0.720 \text{ ms}^{-2}$

$v = ?$ $s = 60.0 \text{ m}$

Consider the motion of B from the 60.0 metre mark.

$v^2 = u^2 + 2as$

$v^2 = 18.0^2 + 2 \times 0.720 \times 60 = 410.4$

$v = \sqrt{410.4} = 20.26 \approx \textbf{20.3ms}^{-1}$

(b)   For B: $v = u + at$

so $20.26 = 18 + 0.72$

so $t = (20.26 - 18) \div 0.72 = 3.139 \text{ s}$

But B reached the 60 m mark 0.100 s after A, so B takes a total time of $3.139 + 0.100 = 3.239 \text{ s}$

A takes $60 \div 18 = 3.333 \text{ s}$ to reach finish, so B wins by 0.094 s

Displacement–Time Graphs

Velocity = gradient of the displacement–time graph.

In the first displacement-time graph below, the displacement increases by equal amounts in equal times over the first 10 seconds. This means that the object is moving with **constant velocity**. In the first 10 seconds the velocity is a constant 4 ms⁻¹. It then remains stationary for 4 seconds and finally moves in the **opposite direction** with a constant velocity of 6.67 ms⁻¹ for 6 seconds. The object has finally arrived back at its starting point; the total displacement is zero.

Note carefully that:

1. the gradient of a **distance–time** graph is the **scalar quantity, speed**.

2. the gradient of a **displacement–time** graph is the **vector quantity, velocity**.

The second displacement–time graph below tells us that the velocity of the object is increasing; ie it is accelerating. To find the **actual (instantaneous)** velocity at any time we need to carefully **draw the tangent** to the curve at that time and calculate its gradient. The tangent is a straight line that **touches** the curve but does not cut it.

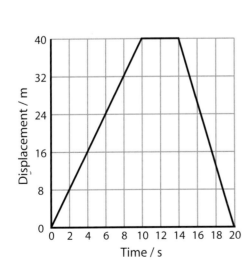
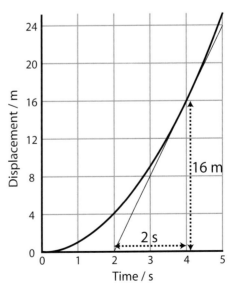

For the graph shown the instantaneous velocity at 4 seconds is the gradient of the tangent to the curve at 4 seconds.

Gradient = $16 \div 2 = 8 \text{ ms}^{-1}$.

Note that for an object undergoing uniform acceleration **from rest,** at any given time the instantaneous velocity at that time is always **twice** the average velocity.

Velocity–Time Graphs

Acceleration

This graph shows the motion of an object that is moving in a straight line and always in the same direction. It starts at rest, accelerates from 0 to 10 seconds, travels at constant velocity for 10 seconds, and then decelerates to a stop after a total time of 25 seconds.

The gradient of the line gives us the acceleration or deceleration.

Between 0 and 10 s the velocity change = 12 ms^{-1}.
Gradient = 12 ÷ 10 = 1.2 ms^{-2}

Between 20 and 25 s the velocity change = −12 ms^{-1}.
Gradient = −12 ÷ 5 = −2.4 ms^{-2}

This **negative acceleration could be described as a deceleration** of 2.4 ms^{-2}.

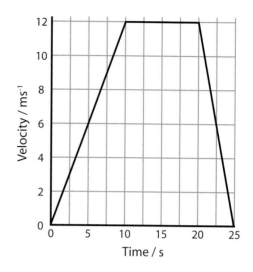

Displacement

From 0 to 10 s:
displacement = average velocity × time taken
= (½ × 12) × 10 = 60 m
= area of triangle

From 10 s to 20 s:
displacement = constant velocity × time taken
= 12 × 10 = 120 m
= area of rectangle

From 20 s to 25 s:
displacement = average velocity × time taken
= (½ × 12) × 5 = 30 m
= area of triangle

So the total distance travelled in 35 s is 60 + 120 + 30 = **210 m**, which is the area of the trapezium. **We conclude that the displacement is the area enclosed between the velocity-time graph and the time axis.**

Note that if the velocity changes from positive to negative it indicates a change in the direction of motion and that has to be taken into account when measuring the displacement. A question in the next exercise provides an example of this.

Variable acceleration

If the object is experiencing a non–uniform acceleration the velocity–time graph is a curve, as shown. As before:
1. the area between the graph and the time axis will give the displacement (first diagram) and
2. the gradient of the curve ($\Delta v/\Delta t$) will give the acceleration at that moment in time (second diagram).

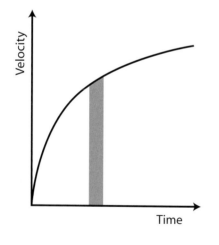

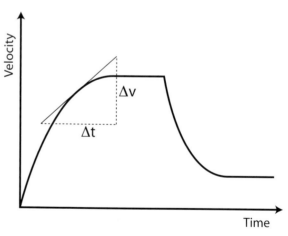

Exercise 3

1. A typical jet aircraft accelerates from rest for 28.0 seconds, leaving the ground with a take-off speed of 270 kilometres per hour.
   (i) Show that a speed of 270 kilometres per hour corresponds to a speed of 75ms^{-1}.
   (ii) Assuming that the acceleration of the aircraft is constant, calculate the acceleration of the aircraft as it travels along the runway and the minimum distance the aircraft travels along the runway before it takes off.
   (CCEA January 2008, amended)

2. An athlete runs a hundred-metre race. He accelerates uniformly from rest for the first 40.0m. He then continues to run the remainder of the race at the velocity attained after the initial period of acceleration. He completes this final part of the race in 4.62 s.

Calculate the total time taken by the athlete for the race. (CCEA January 2007)

3. Below is a velocity–time graph for a car travelling in a straight line along a level road.

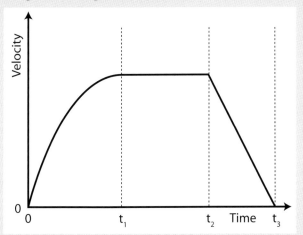

Using the terms **uniform**, **non-uniform**, **zero**, with the words **acceleration** and/or **deceleration**, as appropriate, describe the acceleration or deceleration of the car in the three time intervals indicated.
(CCEA January 2009, amended)

4. A hotel lift, initially at rest, moves vertically in a straight line. From time $t = 0$ it accelerates uniformly until $t = t_1$, when its acceleration suddenly decreases to zero. It continues moving until $t = t_2$ with zero acceleration. It then decelerates uniformly coming to rest at $t = t_3$. The graph below shows how its acceleration depends on time t.

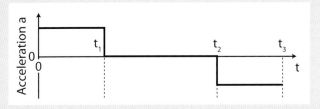

Sketch a graph to show the variation with time t of the velocity v of the lift.
(CCEA January 2008, amended)

Vertical Motion under Gravity

An object dropped will accelerate due to the force of gravity. We can describe an object as being in **free fall** if the **only** force acting on it is gravity.

All objects in free fall accelerate downwards at the same rate independent of the mass of the object. The acceleration due to gravity, g, is approximately 9.81 ms⁻², but its value changes from one point to another over the Earth's surface.

Convention

This book will adopt the convention that **upwards** is **positive** when solving problems relating to motion under gravity. This means that an object moving vertically upwards has a positive velocity, while one moving vertically downwards will have a negative velocity. Objects above the surface have a positive displacement, while objects below the surface have a negative displacement.

Worked Example

A ball is dropped from a height of 10 m onto a hard surface and bounces to a height of 8.5 m. Calculate the time for the ball to hit the hard surface, the speed with which the ball hits it and the ball's speed immediately after the bounce.

Time to fall, from rest, from 10 m:
The ball moves 10 m towards the ground, so the displacement is −10 m.
Since the acceleration is also downwards, $g = -9.81$ ms⁻²
$$S = ut + \tfrac{1}{2} at^2$$
$-10 = 0 + \tfrac{1}{2} \times (-9.81) \times t^2$ giving t = **1.43 s**

Velocity after falling 10 m:
$$v = u + at$$
$v = 0 + (-9.81) \times 1.43$ giving v = **−14.0 ms⁻¹**
where the minus sign shows the ball is moving **towards the ground.**

Initial velocity needed to reach a height of 8.5 m:
The ball is moving upwards, so the displacement and velocity are both positive. But the acceleration due to gravity, g, is towards the ground and is therefore negative.
$$v^2 = u^2 + 2aS$$
$0 = u^2 + 2 \times (-9.81) \times 8.5$ giving u = **12.9 ms⁻¹**

Exercise 4

1. A ball is thrown vertically upwards with an initial velocity of 39.24 ms⁻¹.
   (a) Write down (no calculations required) its speed and its acceleration when it reaches maximum height.
   (b) Calculate the maximum height the ball reaches.
   (c) How long does it take the ball to reach maximum height?

2. A stone is dropped from rest down a well. Exactly 5.00 seconds after the stone is dropped, a splash is heard.
   (a) At what velocity did the stone enter the water?
   (b) Calculate the average speed of the stone as it fell.

   (c) How far did the stone travel before it hit the water?

3. From the top of a tower 30.0 m high, a marble is thrown vertically upwards with an initial speed of 12.0 ms⁻¹. Calculate:
   (a) the maximum height reached above the ground.
   (b) the time taken for the stone to reach maximum height.
   (c) the time taken for the stone to fall from its maximum height to the ground.
   (d) the speed of the stone when it strikes the ground.

4. A helicopter is at a height of 22.0 m and is rising vertically at 4.00 ms^{-1} when it drops a food parcel from a side door.
   (a) Write down the velocity and acceleration of the parcel at the instant it leaves the helicopter and then calculate:
   (b) the maximum height reached by the parcel before it starts to fall towards the ground.
   (c) the velocity of the parcel on impact with the ground.
   (d) the time between the parcel leaving the helicopter and it striking the ground.

Prescribed Experiments

The CCEA Specification for AS 1 gives **five experiments** which you should do and which you must be able to describe. These are the experiments:
• to measure acceleration of free fall (see below)
• to determine the Young modulus
• to determine the I-V characteristics of a metal conductor and an NTC thermistor
• to measure resistivity
• to measure internal resistance

Experiment to Measure the Acceleration of Free Fall, g

The acceleration of free fall can be measured using the apparatus shown. The metal contacts at the top of the apparatus are connected to the start terminals of an electronic timer. A short length of thread attached to the metal ball allows it to be held against the two contacts. When the metal ball is against them the circuit is complete and the clock remains stopped.

When the thread is released, the ball falls, the circuit is broken and the timer starts. When the ball reaches the bottom it strikes and opens a hinged contact, breaking another circuit which causes the timer to stop.

The distance, d, between the bottom of the metal ball and this hinged contact is measured. The distance d is increased from 1.0 m to 2.0 m in steps of 0.1 m and for each distance an average time of fall, t, is determined.

Since the ball starts from rest (u = 0) we can use the equation d = ½gt^2 to find g (ie using s = ut + ½at^2).

Re-arranging this gives g = 2d ÷ t^2.

One approach to finding g is to calculate a value of g for each value of s and t and find an average of g.

Alternatively, a graphical approach can be used. Plotting d on the y axis, and t^2 on the x axis will give a straight line that passes through the origin. If we compare d = ½ gt^2 with the equation for a straight line through the origin, y = mx, we see the gradient is ½g.

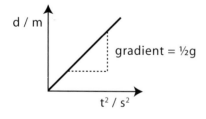

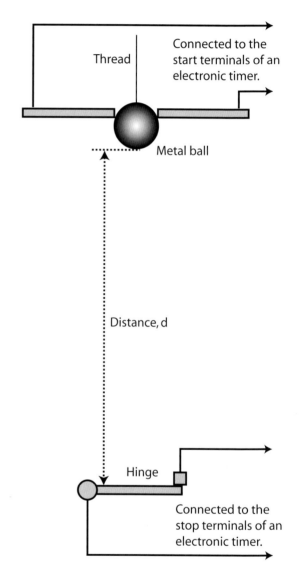

1.4 Dynamics

Students should be able to:

1.4.1 describe projectile motion;

1.4.2 explain motion due to a uniform velocity in one direction and a uniform acceleration in a perpendicular direction;

1.4.3 apply the equations of motion to projectile motion, excluding air resistance;

Projectiles

A **projectile** is any object that is freely moving in the Earth's gravity. However, what follows relates to motion in which there is both a horizontal and a vertical component of velocity. In other words, Section 1.3 related to motion in a single direction; what follows relates to motion in a plane.

Horizontal projection over a cliff

When the projectile leaves the edge of the cliff it begins to fall vertically. Its downward acceleration is 9.81 ms^{-2}. It is treated as an object dropped vertically from rest so that, at any instant, the velocity of the projectile is the resultant of:
(a) the constant horizontal velocity
(b) the vertical velocity gained as it falls

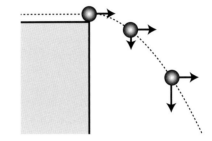

Projectile fired at an angle to the horizontal

Suppose a particle is projected with a velocity u at an angle θ to the horizontal as shown in the diagram below.

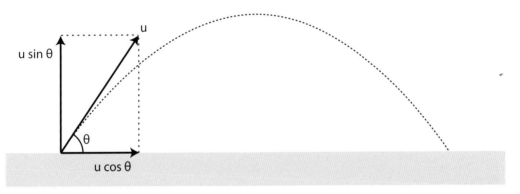

Note carefully that:

1. The **horizontal** component, u cos θ, does not change throughout the motion.

2. The **vertical** component (initially u sin θ), decreases as the projectile moves upwards and increases as it moves downwards.

3. At the maximum height the vertical velocity is momentarily **zero**.

4. The total time in the air is called the **time of flight** and equals twice the time to reach the maximum height.

5. The horizontal distance travelled is called the **range**. Horizontal range = constant horizontal velocity times the time of flight.

6. At any instant the velocity of the projectile is the **resultant** of the constant horizontal velocity and the changing vertical velocity.

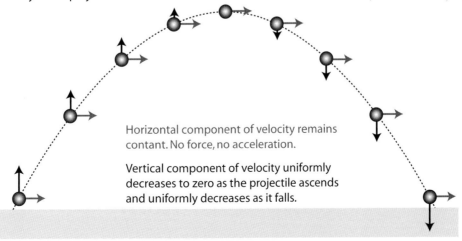

Horizontal component of velocity remains contant. No force, no acceleration.

Vertical component of velocity uniformly decreases to zero as the projectile ascends and uniformly decreases as it falls.

Worked Example

A stone is projected into the air from ground level with a velocity of 25 ms⁻¹ at an angle of 35° to the horizontal.

Calculate:
(a) the time to reach the maximum height
(b) the maximum height reached
(c) the magnitude and direction of the stone's velocity 2.0 s after it was released
(d) the horizontal range.

(a) At the maximum height the vertical component of the projectile's velocity is zero.
The initial vertical velocity = 25 sin 35° = 25 × 0.5736 = 14.34 ms⁻¹.
Using $v = u + at$ we get $0 = 14.34 + (-9.81) t$
$t = 14.34 \div 9.81 = 1.46$ s = time to reach the maximum height

(b) The maximum height can be found by considering the vertical motion.
$S = \frac{1}{2}(u + v)t = \frac{1}{2}(14.34 + 0) \times 1.46 = 10.47$ m

(c) The horizontal component remains constant throughout the motion. Throughout the motion the horizontal component of the projectile's velocity is 25 cos 35° = 20.48 ms⁻¹.
After 2.0 s the vertical component can be calculated using $v = u + at$ where $u = 14.34$, $a = -9.81$ and $t = 2.0$. This gives $v = -5.28$.
The minus is important, because it tells us that the projectile is now moving down with a velocity of 5.28 ms⁻¹.
Projectile's velocity at $t = 2.0$ s $= \sqrt{20.48^2 + (-5.28)^2} = 21.15$ ms⁻¹
The angle of the velocity to the horizontal is θ where $\tan\theta = 5.28 \div 20.48$ giving $\theta = 14.5°$

(d) Time of flight = 2 × time to reach the maximum height = 2 × 1.46 = 2.92 s
Range = Constant horizontal velocity × Time of flight
Range = 20.48 × 2.92 = 59.8 m

Range

The range, R, of a projectile having an initial velocity, u, at an angle θ to the horizontal is given by: $R = (u^2 \sin 2\theta) \div g$

Note that the range depends on the angle of projection θ. The term $\sin 2\theta$ has a maximum value of 1 when $\theta = 45°$.

For a given initial velocity, the range has a maximum value when the angle of projection is 45°.

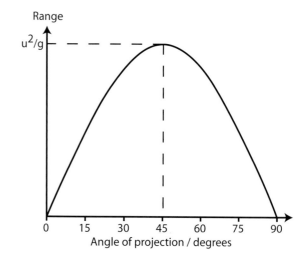

Exercise 5

1. A rugby ball is kicked over the crossbar between the goal-posts from a position 25 m directly in front of the posts, as shown.

   The ball reaches maximum height H above the ground at a position vertically above the crossbar. It takes 1.4 seconds to reach this maximum height. Assume air resistance is negligible.

   (a) Calculate the horizontal and vertical components of velocity at the instant the ball leaves the kicker's foot.

   (b) (i) Use your answers to part (a) to find the magnitude of the initial velocity after the ball is kicked.
   (ii) Find the angle above the horizontal at which the ball is kicked.
   (iii) Find the maximum height H reached by the ball.
   (CCEA June 2009, amended)

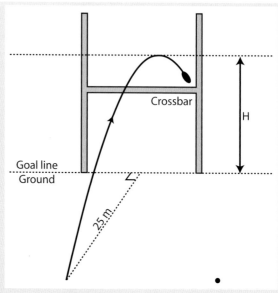

2. When a long jumper completes a jump, his centre of mass is 1.0 m above ground level at take off and 0.4 m above ground level on landing.

The long jumper has studied some physics and has read that in order to make the horizontal distance of his jump as long as possible he should jump at an angle of 45° to the horizontal. The athlete takes off at a speed of 9.3 ms⁻¹ at an angle of 45° to the horizontal.

(i) Calculate the initial vertical velocity of the athlete.

(ii) Show that the vertical component of the velocity of the athlete on landing has magnitude 7.4 ms⁻¹

(iii) Calculate the time spent in the air by the athlete during the jump.

(CCEA June 2011)

1.5 Newton's Laws of Motion

Students should be able to:

1.5.1 state Newton's laws of motion;

1.5.2 apply the laws to simple situations;

1.5.3 recall and use F = ma where mass is constant;

1.5.4 understand that friction is a force that opposes motion;

Newton's First and Second Laws of Motion

Newton's First Law of Motion
If a body is at rest, it will remain at rest unless a resultant force acts on the object. If the body is moving in a straight line with a constant speed, it will continue to move in this way unless a resultant force acts on it.

Newton's Second Law of Motion
The acceleration of an object is inversely proportional to its mass, directly proportional to the resultant force on it and takes place in the same direction as the unbalanced force. Newton's Second Law can be written: F = ma

The unit of force, the **newton**, is defined as the force needed to cause a mass of 1 kg to have an acceleration of 1 ms⁻².

Worked Example

A person stands on a skateboard at the top of a rough sloping track. The total mass of the rider and skateboard is 73 kg.

The track slopes at an angle of 9.5° to the horizontal. The rider and skateboard start from rest and move down the track with uniform acceleration of 0.46 ms⁻². During the motion the force of friction on the board is constant and air resistance is negligible. A simplified diagram of the situation, in which the rider and skateboard have been replaced by a point mass in contact with the track, is shown below.

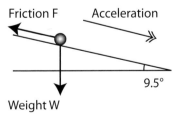

Calculate (i) the magnitude of the resultant force causing the skateboard and rider to accelerate down the slope and (ii) the constant frictional force acting on the skateboard as it moves down the slope.

(i) The resultant force is found using
F = ma, where F is the resultant force.
F = 73 × 0.46 = **33.58 N**

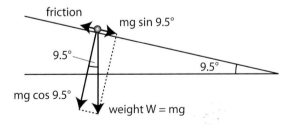

(ii) Resultant force = mg sin 9.5° – Friction
33.58 = 73 × 9.81 × 0.165 – Friction
33.58 = 118.20 – Friction
Friction = **84.6 N**

Newton's Third Law of Motion
If body A exerts a force on body B, then body B exerts a force of the same size on body A, but in the opposite direction.

The forces of an action – reaction pair always **act on different bodies**.

Two forces that act on the same body are not an action – reaction pair, even though they may be equal in magnitude but opposite in direction.

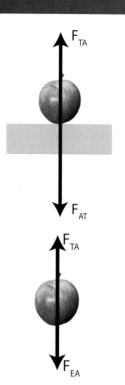

Consider an apple is in contact with a table. The apple exerts a downward force F_{AT} (AT meaning apple on table): call this the action force. The table exerts an upward force on the apple, F_{TA} (TA meaning table on apple): call this is the reaction force. This is an example of the action – reaction pair of forces to which Newton's Third Law refers.

If we look at the forces acting only on the apple, we have F_{EA} (weight of the apple) and F_{TA} the upward supporting force from the table.

The forces F_{EA} and F_{TA} are equal in magnitude and opposite in direction but they act on the same body, the apple. These do not constitute an action – reaction pair because they act on the same object, in this case the apple.

Worked Example

A toy car of mass 400 g is placed on a slope inclined at 25.0° to the horizontal. The diagram shows a simplified diagram of the situation.

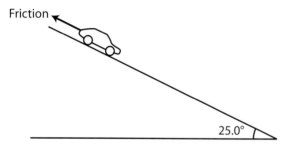

(i) The car is released and starts to move down the slope. The force of friction opposing the motion is 1.20 N. Calculate the initial acceleration of the car down the slope.

(ii) The force of friction increases as the car speeds up. At one stage in the motion the frictional force is increased by 0.46 N. Describe how this affects the acceleration. (CCEA January 2008)

(i) $F_{resultant}$ = mg sin θ – Friction = 0.4 × 9.81 × sin 25° – 1.2
$= 0.46$ N
acceleration = $F_{resultant}$ ÷ mass = 0.46 ÷ 0.4 = 1.13 ms^{-2}

(ii) As the friction force increases, the resultant force decreases and the acceleration decreases. When the friction force reaches 0.46 N, the resultant force is zero and the car stops accelerating: it moves in a straight line with constant velocity.

Worked Example

A man of mass 60.0 kg stands on scales inside a lift. The scales measure the man's weight, not his mass. What readings would you expect to see on the scales when the lift is moving upwards with:

(a) a constant acceleration of 2.00 ms^{-2}?
(b) a constant speed of 2.00 ms^{-1}?
(c) a constant deceleration of 2.00 ms^{-2}?

The reading on the scales is the reaction force, R, as in the sketches below:

(a) When accelerating upwards,
R – mg = ma
R = mg + ma
= 60 × 9.81 + 60 × 2
= 709 N

(b) At constant speed,
R – mg = 0
R = mg = 60 × 9.81
= 589 N

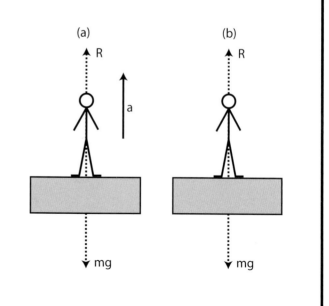

(c) When accelerating downwards,
$$mg - R = ma$$
$$R = mg - ma$$
$$= 60 \times 9.81 - 60 \times 2$$
$$= 469 \text{ N}$$

(c)

Exercise 6

1. A car of mass of 1800 kg is moving with a speed of 16.7 ms⁻¹. The driver applies a constant braking force of 1200 N. Calculate the time interval between the application of the brakes and the car coming to rest.
(CCEA January 2009)

2 (a) A train of mass 2.3×10^6 kg travels at a constant speed of 20 m s⁻¹.
There are opposing forces on the train of 0.6 N for every 1 kg of its mass.
If the train then accelerates at 0.20 ms⁻², calculate the driving force required to overcome these opposing forces and produce this acceleration.

(b) The train now goes onto a section of the track which has been covered by leaves and is slippery as a result. Describe and explain what effect this would have on the motion of the train.
(CCEA January 2010)

3. (a) State Newton's first and third laws of motion.
(b) A student considers a brick resting on the ground as shown below.

He considered the following four forces which he names forces A, B, C and D.
Force A – The normal contact force exerted by the ground on the brick
Force B – The weight of the brick
Force C – The downwards force exerted by the brick on the ground
Force D – The gravitational attraction of the brick on the Earth
(i) Referring to the forces above, explain how Newton's first law applies to the brick.
(ii) Referring to the forces above, explain how Newton's third law applies to the brick and the ground.
(CCEA June 2010)

1.6 Principle of Moments

Students should be able to:

1.6.1 define the moment of a force about a point;

1.6.2 state the principle of moments;

1.6.3 use the principle of moments to solve simple problems;

Moment of a Force

The moment of a force about a point is defined as the product of the force and the perpendicular distance from the point to the line-of-action of the force.

Moment = Force × Perpendicular distance from the point to force

The force is measured in N and the distance in m. Moments are measured in newton–metres, written as Nm. The direction of a moment can be clockwise or anti-clockwise. The moment in the diagram below is **clockwise**.

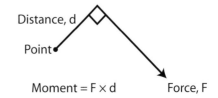

Distance, d

Point

Moment = F × d   Force, F

Worked Example

A mechanic tries to remove a rusted nut from fixed bolt using a spanner of length 0.18 m. When he applies his maximum force of 300 N, the nut does not turn.

By placing a steel tube over the handle of the spanner, the length is increased to 0.27 m. When he applies the same maximum force of 300 N at the end of the steel tube, the nut is just loosened.

Calculate the minimum force that would have been necessary to loosen the nut if the length of the spanner had remained 0.18 m.

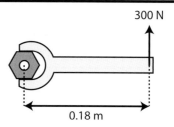

The moment required to loosen the nut is
$$300 \times 0.27 = 81 \text{ Nm}$$

If the force required to loosen the nut, when the length is 0.18 m, is F.

$$F \times 0.18 = 81$$
$$F = 81 \div 0.18 = 450 \text{ N}$$

Couples

A single force acting on an object will make it move off in the direction of the force. A **couple** is two forces that act in opposite directions, not along the same line, and which cause rotation. A couple produces an **unbalanced moment**.

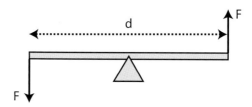

The moment of each force about the pivot is F × ½ d

The sum of these two moments is therefore F × ½ d + F × ½ d = F × d

Moment of a couple = One force × Perpendicular separation of the forces

Centre of Gravity and Centre of Mass

The **centre of gravity** of an object is the point at which we can take its **weight** to act.

The **centre of mass** of an object is the point at which we take its **mass** to be concentrated.

This means that a resultant force acting through the centre of mass would cause the object to move in a straight line without causing it to rotate. For most everyday situations the centre of gravity coincides with the centre of mass.

Principle of Moments

When an object is in rotational equilibrium, the sum of the clockwise moments about any point is equal to the sum of the anticlockwise moments about the same point.

Worked Example

A non-uniform rod of mass 5.50 kg and length 2.00 m is pivoted at a point P at one end of the rod. The rod is held horizontally by a tension of 50.0N acting vertically in a light string fixed to the other end of the rod, as shown. Calculate
(i) the distance of centre of gravity from the point P
(ii) the size and direction of the force acting through point P.

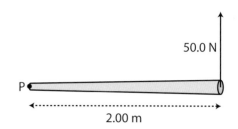

(i) Let the distance from the centre of gravity to the pivot be d.

Then, taking moments about point P,
ACWM = CWM, so 50 × 2 = (5.50 × 9.81) × d,
so d = 100 ÷ 53.955 = 1.85 m

(ii) The weight of the rod is approximately 53.96 N and it acts vertically downwards at the centre of gravity. The total upward forces must balance the total downward forces, so the force through P is **upwards** and of size 3.96 N

Reactions

Many AS questions require the student to **determine the reactions** at points of support. Study carefully the following worked example from an AS paper.

Worked Example

A boy uses a uniform plank of wood of mass 30 kg and length 4.0 m to cross a river. He places one end of the plank on the river bank and rests the plank on a rock in the river as shown in the diagram.

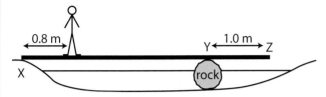

(i) The rock is 1 m from the end of the plank. The boy, who has a mass of 65 kg, stands 0.8 m from the river bank at end X. Calculate the vertical support force, provided by the rock, at Y and the support force provided by the bank, at X.

(ii) Will the boy be able to stand at end Z without the plank rising off the riverbank and the boy falling in the river? Explain your answer.

(CCEA June 2010, amended)

(i) Let the reaction at X be R_X and the reaction at Y be R_Y
To find the reaction at Y, take moments about point X. We do this because the support force at X, R_X, has no moment about X and can therefore be ignored **if** we take moments about X.

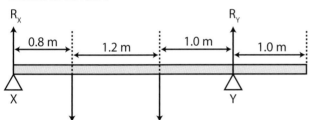

ACWM = CWM **about point X**
$R_Y \times 3 = 30\,g \times 2 + 65\,g \times 0.8$
$R_Y = 366$ N

ACWM = CWM **about point Y**
$R_X \times 3 = 1 \times 30\,g + 2.2 \times 65\,g$
$R_X = 566$ N

Observe that the total downward forces,
$95\,g = 95 \times 9.81 = 932$ N and the total upward forces
$R_X + R_Y = 566 + 366 = 932$ N.
This provides a convenient check that the reactions have been calculated correctly – it also provides an alternative method to calculate one reaction given the other.

(ii) In the diagram the 30 g (N) force and the 65 g (N) force are both 1.0 m away from Y.

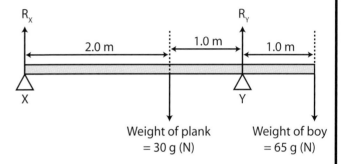

Now, since 65 g > 30 g, there will always be a resultant clockwise moment about point Y. This resultant clockwise moment means that the plank is not in equilibrium and will **tip about Y** by lifting off the bank at X. So the boy is **unable to stand** at point Z without falling into the river.

Exercise 7

1. A stage lighting batten consists of a uniform beam AB, 24 m long, which weighs 600 N. The batten is suspended by two vertical cables C and D.

   The tensions in each cable are equal to 430 N. The batten supports two spotlights S1 and S2 each of weight 70 N and a floodlight F of weight 120 N. The arrangement and distances are shown in the diagram.

   How far is cable C from end A?

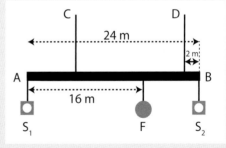

2. A uniform wooden rod AB weighs 1.2 N and is 120 cm long. It rests on two sharp supports at C and D placed 10 cm from each end of the rod. Weights of 0.2 N and 0.9 N hang from loops of thread 30 cm from A and 40 cm from B respectively.

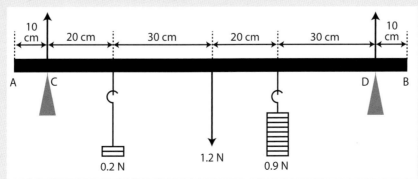

Calculate the reactions at supports C and D and comment on their sum.

3. A wheel of radius 0.50 m rests on a level road at point C and makes contact with the edge E of a kerb of height 0.20 m, as shown in the diagram. A horizontal force of 240 N, applied through the axle of the wheel at X, is required just to move the wheel over the kerb.

   Find the weight of the wheel.

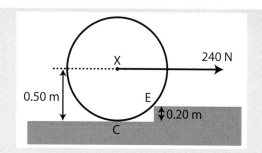

4. A diver stands on the end of an adjustable springboard as shown opposite.

   The diver exerts a moment on the springboard about the pivot at point X.
   (a) On what two factors will the size of the moment the diver exerts depend?

   The total length of the springboard is 4.88 m and the pivot X can be adjusted to move a distance of 0.28 m on either side of its centre position as shown in the diagram.

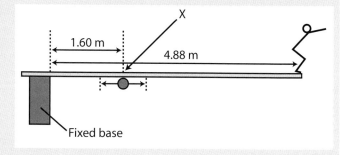

   (b)(i) Show that the **maximum** moment that a diver of mass 65 kg can exert when she stands on the end of the springboard is 2270 N m.

   (ii) A different diver of mass 75 kg now stands on their own on the end of the springboard. By how much, and in what direction, will the pivot need to be moved from its **central position** for this diver to exert the same moment as the 65 kg diver in (b)(i)?
   (CCEA January 2010)

5. (a) (i) State how to calculate the moment of a force about a point.
   (ii) Name the SI unit of the moment of a force.
   (iii) State the principle of moments.
   (b) The diagram opposite shows a stationary wheelbarrow being supported by a gardener who applies a vertical force of 50 N at the end of the handles.

   The weight of the wheelbarrow and contents is 175 N. The force applied to the handles acts at a horizontal distance of 1.40 m from the point of contact of the wheel with the ground.

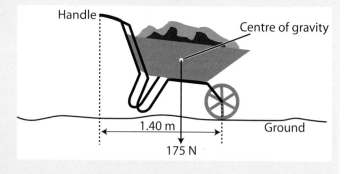

   (i) Another force acts on the wheelbarrow at the wheel. State the magnitude and direction of this force.
   (ii) Calculate the horizontal distance from the centre of gravity to the end of the handle.
   (CCEA June 2009)

6. The diagram opposite shows a uniform plank of weight 30 N and length 3 m, resting on two supports. The supports are 0.5 m and 2.0 m from the left hand end of the plank. A weight of 18 N is suspended from the left hand end of the plank.

   (a) Find the reactions X and Y at the two supports.
   (b) By how much should the weight at the left hand end be increased so that the reaction at Y becomes zero?
   (CCEA January 2011)

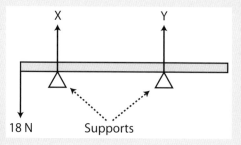

Students should be able to:

1.7.1 define work done, potential energy, kinetic energy, efficiency and power;

1.7.2 recognise that when work is done energy is transferred from one form to another;

1.7.3 calculate the work done for constant forces, including force not along the line of motion;

1.7.4 recall and use the equations Δp.e. = mgΔh and k.e. = $\frac{1}{2}$mv^2;

1.7.5 state the principle of conservation of energy and use it to calculate exchanges between gravitational potential energy and kinetic energy;

1.7.6 recall and use: $P = \dfrac{\text{work done}}{\text{time taken}}$, $P = Fv$,

$\text{efficiency} = \dfrac{\text{useful energy (power) output}}{\text{energy (power) input}}$;

There are five important definitions (1.7.1) and familiar equations have been re-formulated in a more rigorous way (1.7.4). Section 1.7.6 refers to a power equation (P = Fv) with which students are unlikely to be familiar.

Definitions

- We define the **work done** by a constant force as the product of the force and the distance moved in the direction of the force.

  Work done = constant force × distance moved in the direction of the force

  W = F × s

  or **W = Fs cos θ**

  At AS you must be able to apply this new definition when the force and the distance moved are not in the same direction. Study the worked example below.

- A mass has **gravitational potential energy** when it is raised above the ground.

  Δp.e. = mgΔh   where Δp.e. = change in potential energy in J

  m = mass in kg

  g = acceleration of free fall in ms^{-2}

  Δh = vertical distance in m

  This new form of the equation emphasises the fact that we can only measure the change in gravitational potential energy.

- A moving object possesses **kinetic energy**.

  k.e. = $\frac{1}{2}$ mv^2   where   k.e. = kinetic energy in J

  m = mass of the object in kg

  v = speed in ms^{-1}

  The work done by a force accelerating a mass m from a speed u to a speed v is given by: $W = \frac{1}{2} mv^2 - \frac{1}{2} mu^2$

- **Efficiency** is defined as the ratio of useful output work (or power) to total input work (or power).

  $\text{efficiency} = \dfrac{\text{useful energy (power) output}}{\text{energy (power) input}}$

  Efficiency is a number between 0 and 1 (in accordance with the Law of Conservation of Energy). It has no units.

- **Power** is defined as the rate of doing work. The definition can be expressed by the equation:

  $P = \dfrac{\text{work done}}{\text{time taken}}$

  Students learn this equation at GCSE. An alternative is:

  $P = \dfrac{\text{energy transferred}}{\text{time taken}}$

- Since W = Fs and P = W÷t, we have P = Fs÷t. But s÷t = velocity, v. Hence:

  P = Fv   where   P = power in watts (W)

  F = force being applied in newtons (N)

  v = constant speed at which force is moving in ms^{-1}

In recent years examiners have sometimes asked questions relating to **mechanical energy**. Mechanical energy is the sum of the kinetic energy and potential energy. When there is an increase in mechanical energy, work has had to be done by some external agent, such as a car engine. When there is a reduction in mechanical energy, this can be used to do work against frictional forces. In the general case, work is done against friction **and** work is supplied by an external agent.

The general equation is well worth remembering:

Increase in mechanical energy + **work done against friction** = **work supplied from external sources**

If the mechanical energy decreases, then we treat it as negative in the equation above.

Worked Example

A cyclist and her machine have a mass of 77.0 kg. She travels a total distance of 800m between two hills. At the top of the higher hill her velocity is 6.20 ms⁻¹. She descends the hill and ascends to the top of the next hill where her velocity is 5.10 ms⁻¹. Throughout the distance travelled the cyclist contends with an average opposing force of 17.0 N.

(i) Air resistance is a possible cause for a force which the cyclist must expend energy to overcome. Suggest two other forces which must also be overcome.

(ii) Calculate (a) the total change of mechanical energy of the cyclist between the two hill tops and (b) the energy contributed by the cyclist for the complete journey between the two hills where the average opposing force of 17.0N was encountered.   *(CCEA January 2007)*

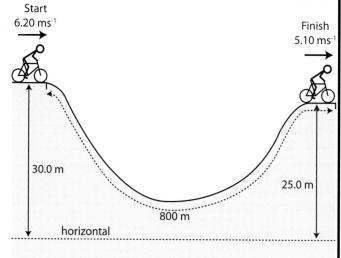

(i) Friction between tyres and the road and the force of gravity (when ascending the hill)

(ii) (a) Mechanical energy at start = GPE + KE

$= (77 \times 9.81 \times 30 + \frac{1}{2} \times 77 \times 6.2^2) = 24\,141$ J

Mechanical energy at end = GPE + KE

$= (77 \times 9.81 \times 25 + \frac{1}{2} \times 77 \times 5.1^2) = 19\,886$ J

Total reduction in mechanical energy = 24 141 – 19 886 = **4255 J**

(b) **Increase in mechanical energy** + **work done against friction** = **work supplied from external sources**

–4255   + 17 × 800   = Energy contributed by cyclist

Energy to overcome resistance forces = F × d = 800 × 17 = 13 600 J

Energy contributed by cyclist (external source) = 13 600 – 4255 = **9345 J**

Worked Example

An explorer dragging a sledge of mass 70 kg across a frozen lake. The explorer attaches the rope to his waist and the force of 200 N is applied at 30° to the horizontal.

(a) How much work is done by the explorer in dragging the sledge 150 metres across the ice at a steady speed of 4 ms⁻¹?

(b) Calculate the kinetic energy of the sledge at this speed.

(c) Dragging the sledge over 150 metres generates 4000 J of heat energy and 20 J of sound energy. Calculate the efficiency of the sledge.

(d) Calculate the explorer's useful output power.

(a) The difficulty here is that the force, F (200 N), and the displacement, s, are not in the same direction. The easiest solution is to resolve the 200 N force into its vertical and horizontal components as shown below.

Work done = constant force × distance moved in direction of the force

= 173.2 N × 150 m = 25 980 J

(b) KE = ½ mv² = ½ × 70 × 4² = 560 J

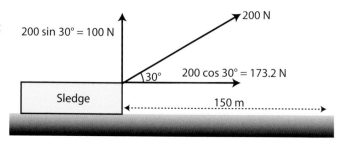

(c) Useful output work = 25 980 J

Total work produced = work against friction + heat + sound

$$= 25\,980 + 4000 + 20 = 30\,000 \text{ J}$$

$$\text{Efficiency} = \frac{\text{useful work output}}{\text{total energy input}} = \frac{25\,980}{30\,000} = 0.866$$

(d) Time taken to drag sledge 150 m at 4 ms⁻¹ is

$$150 \div 4 = 37.5 \text{ s}$$

$$\text{Useful output power} = \frac{\text{useful work done}}{\text{time taken}} = \frac{25\,980}{37.5} = 693 \text{ W}$$

Worked Example

The dam at a certain hydroelectric power station is 170 m deep. The electrical power output from the generators at the base of the dam is 2000 MW. Given that 1 kg of water has a volume of 0.001 m³, calculate the minimum rate at which water leaves the dam in m³s⁻¹ when electrical generation takes place at this rate.

In 1 s, the potential energy converted to electrical energy is

$$2 \times 10^3 \text{ MJ} = 2 \times 10^9 \text{ J}$$

Change in gravitational Δp.e. = $mg\Delta h$

$$= m \times 9.81 \times 170 = 1667.7 \times m$$

So mass removed from dam every second is

$$(2 \times 10^9) \div 1667.7 \approx 1.20 \times 10^6 \text{ kg}$$

Since each kilogram of water has a volume of 0.001 m³, the rate of flow is

$$(1.2 \times 10^6) \times 0.001 = 1200 \text{ m}^3\text{s}^{-1}$$

Exercise 8

1. A car of mass 1200 kg has an output power of 60 kW when travelling at a speed of 30 ms⁻¹ along a flat road. What power output is required if the same car is to travel at the same speed up a hill of gradient 10%? (Such a hill has a slope angle of tan⁻¹(0.1) or 5.7°.)

2. An electric motor has an output power of 2400 W and is used to raise a ship's anchor. If the tension in the cable is 8 kN, at what constant speed is the anchor being raised?

3. (a) Distinguish between kinetic energy and gravitational potential energy.

(b) A particle possesses energy in two forms only: kinetic energy and gravitational energy. It has a total energy of 3.0 J and is initially at rest. Its potential energy E_p changes causing a corresponding change in its kinetic energy E_k. No external work is done on or by the system. Copy the grid and draw a graph of kinetic energy E_k against potential energy E_p.

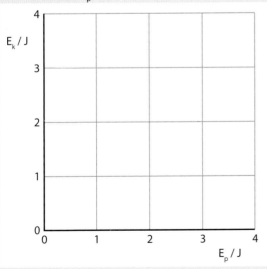

Explain how your graph illustrates the principle of conservation of energy.

(c) An AS Physics student plans to enter for the high jump event at the School Sports. She estimates that, if she is to have a chance of winning, she will have to raise her centre of mass by 1.6 m to clear the bar. She will also have to move her centre of mass horizontally at a speed of 0.80 ms⁻¹ at the top of her jump in order to roll over the bar.
(i) The student's mass is 75 kg. Estimate the total energy required to raise her centre of mass and roll over the bar.
(ii) The student assumes that this energy can be supplied entirely from the kinetic energy she will have at the end of her run-up. Estimate the minimum speed she will require at the end of the run-up.
(CCEA June 2006)

4. A filament lamp rated 60 W has an efficiency of 0.04 (4%). A modern long-life lamp is rated 12 W and produces the same useful output power as the filament lamp. Calculate
(a) the useful output power of the filament lamp and
(b) the efficiency of the long-life lamp.

5. To enable a train to travel at a steady speed of 30 ms⁻¹ along a level track, the engine must supply a pulling force of 50 kN.
(a) How much work is the engine doing every second?
(b) If the power is proportional to the cube of the velocity, how much power is needed to drive the train at a speed of 40 ms⁻¹?

6. A cyclist starts from rest at the top of a hill which has a vertical height of 8 m. As she freewheels down the hill, 15% of her energy is dissipated as heat due to friction. The combined mass of the bicycle and cyclist is 90 kg.

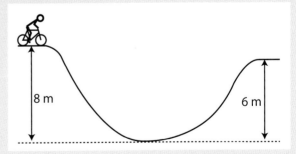

(i) Calculate the speed with which she reaches the bottom of the hill.
(ii) The cyclist starts to pedal at the bottom of the next hill which is 6 m high. She reaches the top of this hill at a speed of 8.9 ms⁻¹. Assuming there are no energy losses after the cyclist reaches the bottom of the first hill, calculate how much work the cyclist does as she pedals to the top of the second hill.
(CCEA January 2010)

1.8 Deformation of Solids

Students should be able to:

1.8.1 state Hooke's law and use f = kx to solve simple problems;

1.8.2 understand the terms elastic and plastic deformation and elastic limit;

1.8.3 distinguish between limit of proportionality and elastic limit;

1.8.4 define the terms stress, strain, ultimate tensile stress;

1.8.5 define the Young modulus;

1.8.6 perform and describe an experiment to determine the Young modulus;

Hooke's Law

At GCSE the 'elastic limit' and the 'limit of proportionality' were treated as meaning the same thing. In fact, this is not so and at AS level we must make the distinction clear. Hooke's Law states that:

Up to a maximum load, known as the limit of proportionality, the extension of an elastic material is proportional to the applied load.

Hooke's Law may be written as an equation:

$$F = kx$$

where F = applied load in N,

k = the Hooke's Law constant in Nm^{-1}

x = the extension of the specimen under test in m

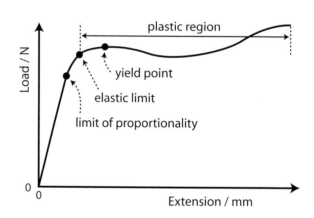

The graph opposite illustrates how the load and extension are related for a typical metal wire. From (0,0) up to the limit of proportionality the line is straight. This is the region where the wire obeys Hooke's Law. Beyond the **limit of proportionality**, the line curves. A point is then reached where any further load will cause the wire to become **permanently** stretched. This is the **elastic limit**.

The elastic limit is therefore the maximum load a specimen can experience and still return to its original length when the deforming force is removed. Beyond the elastic limit the wire reaches a 'yield point'. The internal molecular structure is being permanently changed as crystal planes slide across each other. **A wire stretched beyond its elastic limit** is said to be 'plastic' and may stretch enormously before it finally breaks.

Exercise 9

1. A metal cube of side 200 mm is held in a vice. Each turn of the handle of the vice moves the jaws 0.500 mm closer together. The vice is tightened up by a quarter turn. A strain gauge attached to the metal shows the compressive force to be 600 kN. Assuming the metal obeys Hooke's Law at this compression, calculate the reduction in the length of the metal and its stiffness constant, k.

2. Two identical springs are joined in series. One has a spring constant of 12 Ncm^{-1} and the other has a spring constant of 18 Ncm^{-1}. One free end is connected to a fixed point and from the other a weight of 36 N is applied.
(i) State the tension in each spring.
(ii) Calculate the extension in the combination caused by the 36 N load and the spring (Hooke's Law) constant of the combination.

3. (a) State Hooke's law.
(b) A spring that obeys Hooke's law has a length of 8 cm when a load of 2 N is attached to it and a length of 14 cm when a load of 6 N is attached. Calculate the spring constant of the spring and state its units.
(CCEA June 2011, amended)

Stress, Strain and Young Modulus

The definitions of these quantities need to be learned in preparation for the AS examination. All of them can be expressed as equations, where:

σ = stress in Pa

ε = strain (no units)

E = Young Modulus in Nm^{-2}

F is the applied force in N

A is the cross section area of specimen in m^2

ΔL = extension of specimen

L_o = original length of specimen

- **Stress** (σ) is defined as the applied force per unit area of cross section.

$$\sigma = \frac{F}{A}$$

- **Strain** (ε) is defined as the ratio of the change in the length of a specimen to its original length.

$$\varepsilon = \frac{\Delta L}{L_0}$$

- Within the limit of proportionality, the ratio of stress to strain is defined as the **Young Modulus** (E).

$$E = \frac{\sigma}{\varepsilon}$$

Measuring the Young Modulus of a Metal

The method below uses two long wires suspended from a common support in the ceiling. One wire is called the reference wire because the extension of the wire under test is measured with respect to it. Both the reference wire and the wire under test should be made of the same material, have the same cross-section area and be approximately the same length.

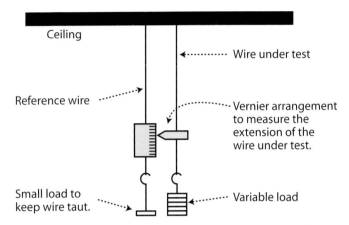

The wires should be as long as possible (at least 2 m) so as to obtain the greatest possible extension of the test wire.

The length, L, of the test wire is measured in mm using a metre stick.

The measurement should be taken from the point of suspension to the Vernier scale. Using a micrometer screw gauge, the diameter, d, of the test wire is measured at about six places spread out along its length. We measure the diameter in this way to avoid the possibility of small kinks in the wire giving rise to erroneous results. The cross section area, A, can then be found from the equation $A = \frac{1}{4}\pi\langle d\rangle^2$ where $\langle d\rangle$ is the average diameter of the wire. The reference wire is then loaded with about 5 N to keep it taught. The test wire is loaded in steps of 10 N from 10 N to about 100 N. For each load on the test wire, the extension is found from the Vernier and the stress, σ, ($\sigma = F \div A$) and strain, ε, ($\varepsilon = \Delta L \div L_0$) calculated and recorded in a suitable table.

Typical Results for Young Modulus Experiment on a Metal Wire

Length of test wire / m: 2.055			
Diameter of test wire / mm: 1.38, 1.38, 1.37, 1.39, 1.38, 1.38			
Average diameter of test wire / mm: 1.38			
Area of cross section / m²: 1.496×10^{-6}			
F / N	**ΔL / mm**	**σ / MPa**	**$\varepsilon \times 10^{-4}$**
10	0.07	6.68	0.334
20	0.14	13.37	0.668
30	0.21	20.05	1.003
40	0.27	26.74	1.337
50	0.34	33.42	1.671
60	0.41	40.11	2.005
70	0.48	46.79	2.340
80	0.55	53.48	2.674
90	0.62	60.16	3.008
100	0.69	66.84	3.342

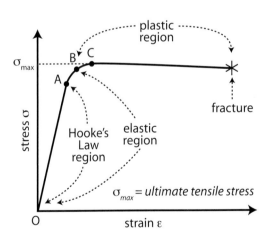

This is the second of five experiments prescribed by the AS 1 specification which **candidates must be able to describe**. The reader should use the results of the above experiment to plot a graph of stress σ (y-axis) against strain ε (x-axis) and draw the straight line of best fit. The gradient of this **straight line** is the Young Modulus.

The gradient of the straight line region (OA) is the Young Modulus.

If we continued to measure stress and strain for increasing loads on a wire, we would be able to plot a graph like the one shown above. Point A represents the limit of proportionality. Point B represents the elastic limit. Point C marks the position of **ultimate tensile stress** (UTS), defined as the maximum stress which can be applied to a wire without it breaking.

Exercise 10

1. A copper wire, of length L and cross-sectional area A, is stretched by a force F causing it to increase in length by an amount e.
   (a) The Young modulus E of the copper is the ratio of the stress in the wire to the strain of the wire.
   Obtain an expression for the Young modulus, E, in terms of L, A, F and e.
   (b) Describe an experiment to determine the Young modulus of copper.
   (CCEA June 2010)

2. A student carried out an experiment to investigate the stretching of a spring as various masses were added to provide the stretching force. The results obtained are shown in the table. The original length of the spring was 5.2 cm.

Mass added / kg	Load / N	Length of spring / cm	Extension / cm
1.00		6.1	
2.00		7.0	
3.00		7.9	
4.00		8.8	
5.00		9.7	

(a) Calculate values for the load and extension and fill in the columns in the table.
(b) (i) Use values from the table to prove that load is directly proportional to extension and hence calculate a value for the spring constant, k.
(ii) How could a value of k be obtained graphically from these results?
(CCEA January 2010)

3. (a) Draw and label an experimental arrangement which could be used to measure the Young modulus of the material of a long wire.
   (b) A stretching force of 5.5N is applied to a copper wire of length 2.5m, producing a strain of 7.8×10^{-4}. The Young Modulus of copper is 1.2×10^{11} Nm^{-2}.
   (i) Calculate the extension produced in the wire.
   (ii) Calculate the cross-sectional area of the wire in mm^2.
   (CCEA January 2011)

1.9 Electric Current and Charge

Students should be able to:

1.9.1 describe current as the rate of flow of charge;

1.9.2 recall and use the equation $I = \dfrac{\Delta Q}{\Delta t}$;

Conduction in Solids

In metallic conductors the carriers are 'free' electrons. The 'free' electrons in a metal are in rapid, random motion, with **thermal speeds around 1×10^6 ms^{-1}**. Since this motion is random, we do not observe an electric current.

When a battery is applied across the ends of a conductor, the electrons accelerate towards the region of positive potential and to gain kinetic energy. Electron collisions with the vibrating atoms cause the electrons to slow down and give up some of their kinetic energy to the atoms themselves. Externally, we observe this increased internal energy as a temperature rise in the conductor. **Electrical resistance is explained by collisions between the 'free electrons' and the vibrating atoms** of the metal.

Following any collision, the electrons accelerate once again and the process continues. There is a **drift of negative charge** towards the region of positive potential. **It is this drift of electrical charge which constitutes an electric current in a metal.** A typical drift velocity is less than 1 mms^{-1}.

Current and Charge

By convention current flows from the region of positive potential to that of lower potential. The current in metals is entirely due to the motion of electrons in the opposite direction to that of the conventional current. The quantity of electric charge flowing past a fixed point is defined in terms of the current.

Thus, for a constant current I flowing for a time Δt we can write:

$\Delta Q = I \times \Delta t$ or $I = \Delta Q \div \Delta t$

where ΔQ = charge flowing past a fixed point, in coulombs
   I = constant current in Amperes
   Δt = time taken for charge to flow past fixed point in seconds

This tells us that:

1. an electric current is the electric charge passing a fixed point in one second

2. a current of 1A flowing in a circuit is equal to a charge of 1C passing a fixed point in the circuit every second.

Worked Example

If the charge on a single electron is −1.6 × 10⁻¹⁹ C, how many electrons flow past a fixed point every minute when a current of 2 A is flowing?

$\Delta Q = I \times \Delta t = 2 \times 60 = 120$ C

   (note the substitution of 60 seconds for 1 minute)

Number of electrons = Total Charge ÷ Charge on a single electron

   $= 120 \div 1.6 \times 10^{-19} = 7.5 \times 10^{20}$ electrons

Worked Example

What steady current flows when a charge of 300 mC flows past a fixed point in 5 s?

$I = \Delta Q \div \Delta t = 300 \times 10^{-3} \div 5$

   $= 60 \times 10^{-3}$ A $= 60$ mA

Worked Example

When a switch in an electrical circuit is closed, a bulb lights instantly, regardless of its distance from the battery. Explain why there is no time delay due to the distance between the lamp and the battery.

Electron drift begins **instantly** at **all** points in the circuit.

Exercise 11

1. The battery in a mobile phone takes exactly 3 hours to charge when the charging current is 400 mA.
   (a)(i) Calculate the charge which is transferred to the battery in this time.
     (ii) Calculate the number of electrons transferred to the battery in this time.
   (b) Early transmissions of information across the Atlantic Ocean through a submarine cable involved the use of direct current signals. Calculations show that the drift speed of the electrons is such that it would take about 200 years for an electron to cross the Atlantic! Explain why there is no such delay in sending information across the Atlantic in this way.
   (CCEA January 2008)

2. (a) Define electric current.
   (b) 5.0×10^{20} electrons pass normally through a cross-section of a wire in 25 s. Find the current in the wire.
   (c) A number of electrons travel between two electrodes in an evacuated tube. This flow of electrons may be considered to be an electron beam current. The mean speed of the electrons is 8.0×10^6 ms⁻¹ and the distance between the two electrodes is 0.45 m. The electron beam current is 1.85 mA.
   (i) Calculate the time taken for an electron to travel between the two electrodes at this speed.
   (ii) Hence calculate the number of electrons in the beam at any instant.
   (CCEA January 2009)

1.10 Potential Difference and Electromotive Force

You should be able to:

1.10.1 recall and use the equations $V = \dfrac{W}{q}$, $V = \dfrac{P}{I}$;

1.10.2 define the volt;

1.10.3 define electromotive force;

1.10.4 distinguish between electromotive force and potential difference;

Electromotive Force (e.m.f.)

We picture a battery as a pump which moves electrons from the negative to the positive terminals around a circuit. A battery does **work** on charges, so **energy must be changed within it.** A battery or generator is said to produce an electromotive force (e.m.f.), defined in terms of energy change.

The **electromotive force (e.m.f.)** of a battery is defined as **the energy converted into electrical energy when unit charge (1 C) passes through it.**

$\text{e.m.f.} = \dfrac{\text{electrical energy converted}}{\text{electric charge moved}}$ $E = \dfrac{W}{Q}$

where   E = e.m.f. in V (volts)
        W = electrical energy converted in J (joules)
        Q = charge in C (coulombs)

The unit of e.m.f., like the unit of potential difference (p.d.), is the volt. The volt can be thought of as a joule per coulomb or a watt per ampere.

Remember:

1. The potential difference between two points is the energy generated for every coulomb passing between them.
2. The potential difference between two points is 1 volt if, when 1 coulomb passes between them, 1 joule of energy is generated.

Distinction Between e.m.f. and p.d.

Although e.m.f. and potential difference have the same unit, they deal with different aspects of an electric circuit.

- **Electromotive force** applies to **a source** supplying electrical energy.
- **Potential difference** refers to the **conversion** of electrical energy to **other energy forms** by a device in a circuit.

The term 'e.m.f.' is misleading since it measures **energy per unit charge** and not force.

A voltmeter measures p.d. A voltmeter connected across the terminals of an electrical supply, such as a battery, records the **terminal p.d.** of the battery.

Some people prefer to think of e.m.f. of a battery as **the p.d. across its terminals when no current is drawn from it**. Our definition of the volt allows us to write:

W = QV

where   W = work done in J (joules)
         Q = charge moved in C (coulombs)
         V = p.d. in V (volts)

All sources of e.m.f. have an **internal resistance** from which the source cannot be separated. When the source provides an electrical current to some external load resistor, a voltage is also developed across this internal resistance. The difference between the e.m.f., E, and the voltage across the external load resistor, V, is equal to the voltage lost in the internal resistor.

Electrical Power

Electrical power is defined as **the rate at which electrical energy is converted into other forms of energy by a circuit or a component, such as a resistor, in a circuit.**

Electrical power, like mechanical power, is measured in watts (W). If we divide both sides of the equation W = QV by time, t, we arrive at:

P = IV

where   P = power in W (watts)
         I = current in A (amperes)
         V = potential difference in V (volts)

Worked Example

An electron in a cathode ray tube is accelerated from rest through a potential difference of 150 kV.
(a) Calculate the KE of the electrons when they collide with the screen.
(b) If the current is 32 mA, how many electrons strike the screen per second?
(c) At what rate must heat be dissipated from the screen when it reaches its working temperature?

(a) $W = QV = 1.6 \times 10^{-19} \times 150 \times 10^3 = $ **2.4×10^{-14} J**

(b) From the definition of charge, the total charge arriving per second = 3.2 mC
Since the charge on each electron is (–) 1.6×10^{-19} C, the number of electrons arriving per second
$= (3.2 \times 10^{-3}) \div (1.6 \times 10^{-19}) = $ **2×10^{16}**.

(c) $P = IV = 3.2 \times 10^{-3} \times 150 \times 10^3 = $ **480 W**

Exercise 12

1. Terms often used in describing an electrical power source, such as a battery, are **terminal potential difference** and **electromotive force (e.m.f.)**. Write a short explanation of these terms and when it is appropriate to use them.   (CCEA June 2009)

2. A fully charged 12 V battery can deliver 1 A for 20 hours. Calculate for the fully charged battery the total charge stored and the total energy stored.

Students should be able to:

1.11.1 describe the relationship between current, voltage and resistance in series and parallel circuits;

1.11.2 state Ohm's law;

1.11.3 recall and use the equations $R = \dfrac{V}{I}$ and $P = I^2R$

1.11.4 define resistivity;

1.11.5 recall and use the equation $R = \dfrac{\rho l}{A}$;

1.11.6 perform and describe an experiment to measure resistivity;

1.11.7 demonstrate knowledge and simple understanding of superconductivity;

1.11.8 distinguish between ohmic and non-ohmic behaviour;

1.11.9 perform experiments to determine the current–voltage characteristics for a metallic conductor and a negative temperature coefficient (ntc) thermistor;

1.11.10 sketch and explain the variation with temperature of the resistance of a pure metallic conductor and a negative temperature coefficient (ntc) thermistor;

1.11.11 appreciate the existence of internal resistance of sources and understand the simple consequences of internal resistance for external circuits;

1.11.12 use the equation $V = E - Ir$;

1.11.13 perform and describe an experiment to measure internal resistance;

Current-Voltage Relationship

The ammeter-voltmeter circuit shown below allows us to vary and measure the p.d. V across a bulb and measure the corresponding current I. By replacing the bulb with another component such as length of wire or a thermistor the circuit can be used to obtain voltage and current measurements for that component.

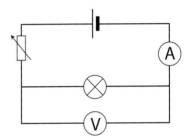

Ohm's Law

Ohm's Law states that the **current through a metallic conductor is directly proportional to the applied p.d., provided the temperature is constant.** These materials are called **ohmic conductors**. We show the relationship as a graph of voltage on the x-axis and current on the y-axis.

Metals and their alloys give I-V graphs which are straight lines through the origin, provided the temperature remains constant. A graph of I against V is called the characteristic of the component. Since I is directly proportional to V, it follows that V÷I = a constant.

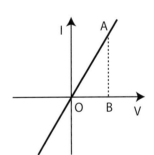

The ratio V/I is called the **resistance**, R of a conductor and is measured in ohms (Ω). Resistance is calculated using the formula:

$$R = \frac{V}{I}$$

where R = resistance in Ω (ohms)
  V = potential difference in V (volts)
  I = current in A (amperes)

In section 1.10, that we were able to write the familiar equation for electrical power, P = IV. We can combine this equation with that for Ohm's Law to give:

$$P = IV = I^2R = \frac{V^2}{R}$$

Collectively, these equations are known as **Joule's Law** of electrical heating.

Worked Example

A train of mass 100 000 kg operates from a 25 kV supply and can accelerate to a speed of 20 ms⁻¹ in 50 seconds along a level stretch of track. Calculate the average current it uses, assuming no energy losses.

Average mechanical power = k.e. ÷ time
  = ½ × 100 000 × 20² ÷ 50 = 400 000 W

I = P÷V = 400 000 ÷ 25 000 = **16 A**

Worked Example

An electric boiler is rated 2645 W and has a heating element of resistance 20 Ω. Calculate the resistance of its heating element.

$P = I^2R$, so $2645 = I^2 \times 20$, thus
$I = \sqrt{2645 \div 20} = \sqrt{132.25} = 11.5\,A$

Current, Voltage and Resistance in Series and Parallel Circuits

Resistors in Series

The **current** in a series circuit is the same everywhere.

The **supply voltage** is equal to the sum of the voltages across each of the series components:

$V_{battery} = V_1 + V_2 + V_3 + \ldots$

The **total resistance** is the sum of the resistance of each component:

$R_T = R_1 + R_2 + R_3 + \ldots$
  = (Battery voltage) ÷ (Battery current)

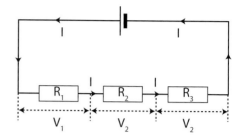

Resistors in Parallel

The **p.d.** across each resistor is the same.

The sum of the **currents** through each resistor is equal to the total current taken from the supply.

$I_{battery} = I_1 + I_2 + I_3 + \ldots$

The **parallel** resistance formula giving the **total resistance**, R_T is:

$\dfrac{1}{R_T} = \dfrac{1}{R_1} + \dfrac{1}{R_2} + \dfrac{1}{R_3} + \ldots$

When there are **just two resistors** the equation above for R_T reduces to:

$R_T = \dfrac{R_1 \times R_2}{R_1 + R_2}$

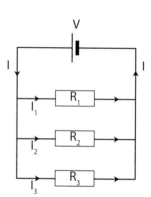

It is important to remember that:

1. the **total resistance** of any **series** arrangement is always **greater than the largest resistance** in that network
2. the **total resistance** of any **parallel** arrangement is always **less than the smallest resistance** in the parallel network
3. the **total resistance of N equal resistors R,** arranged in parallel, is **R ÷ N**

Worked Example

Hybrid circuits *consist of a mixture of parallel and series elements, such as the one shown. Find the total resistance of the combination.*

Applying the series equation first gives the resistance of the 2 Ω and 4 Ω as 6 Ω.

Now applying the equation for parallel networks,

$\dfrac{1}{R_T} = \dfrac{1}{R_1} + \dfrac{1}{R_2} = \dfrac{1}{6} + \dfrac{1}{3} = \dfrac{1}{2}$

Hence, $R_T = 2\,\Omega$.

We can verify this result by calculating the current in each branch.

The voltage across the 3 Ω resistor
= the voltage across the 2 Ω + 4 Ω combination = 12 V

The current in each of the series elements is given by I = V÷R = 12÷6 = 2 A.

The current in the 3 Ω resistor is similarly 12÷3 = 4 A.

The current drawn from the battery, $I_b = V_b \div R_T = 12 \div 2 = 6\,A$, which is the sum (2 A + 4 A) of the currents in the parallel branches of the circuit.

Potential Difference

For a current to flow through a conductor there must be a potential difference across its ends. Now consider the resistance networks shown below. The resistance of each of the two networks is 6 Ω and the current taken from each battery is 3 A. In each case the current flowing from X to B is 2 A and the current flowing from X to C is 1 A. In each network, point X is at a potential of 18 V and Y is at a potential of 0 V.

Diagram A	Diagram B
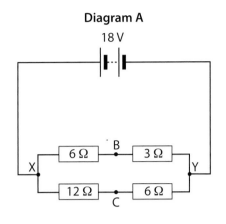	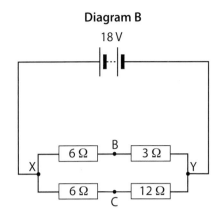

However:

In **Network A**	In **Network B**
• The p.d. from X to B is 12 V, and the p.d. from X to C is also 12 V.	• The p.d. from X to B is 12 V, and the pd. from X to C is 6 V.
• Points B and C are both therefore at a potential of 6 V.	• Points B and C are at potentials of 6 V and 12 V respectively.
• The p.d. between B and C is 0 V.	• The p.d. between B and C is 6 V.
• **Hence, no current will flow in a short wire of negligible resistance connected between B and C, i.e. because the p.d. is zero.**	• **If a wire of negligible resistance connected between B and C, current will flow from C (higher potential) to B (lower potential).**

Questions relating to this topic are frequently seen in AS papers. For further examples see the exercise which follows.

Exercise 13

1. Four identical 6 Ω resistors are connected together in several different arrangements. The diagram below shows one arrangement of the resistors.

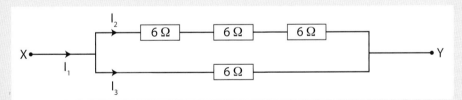

   (a)(i) Calculate the total resistance between terminals X and Y.
      (ii) State the relationship between I_1, I_2 and I_3.
      (iii) The value of current I_1 is 6 A. Determine the current I_3.

   (b) The diagram below shows a different arrangement of the resistors.

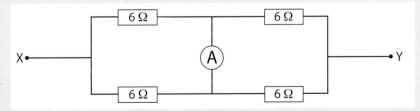

   If the p.d. between X and Y is 10 V, find the current in the ammeter.
   (CCEA June 2010, part)

2. A battery of e.m.f. 12 V and negligible internal resistance is connected to a resistor network, as shown in the circuit diagram.

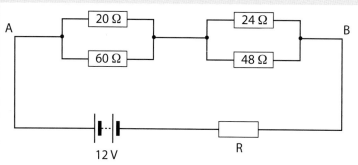

(a) Show clearly that the resistance of the single equivalent resistor that could replace the four resistors between the points A and B is 31 Ω.

(b) The current delivered by the battery is 300 mA. Calculate the total circuit resistance.

(c) Hence find the value of the resistance of the resistor R.

(d) Find the current in the 48 Ω resistor.

(CCEA June 2009)

Ohmic & Non-Ohmic Behaviour

If the temperature of a metal wire is allowed to rise with increasing current, as occurs in the filament of a lamp, then the I-V characteristic curve is as shown on the right. This means that with increasing current (and hence increasing temperature) the resistance of a metal wire increases. However, as the temperature is increasing, the conditions pertaining to Ohm's Law are not constant, so we call this **non-Ohmic behaviour.**

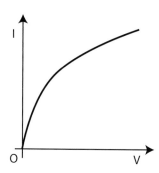

Thermistors

Thermistors are made of semiconductor materials such as silicon or germanium. The I-V characteristic curve for a thermistor is shown on the right. **The resistance of this thermistor decreases as it heats up**.

The symbol for a thermistor is:

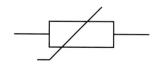

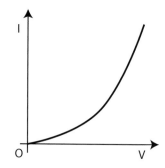

Variation of Resistance of a Metal and an NTC Thermistor with Temperature

The resistance of a metal rises linearly with temperature, as shown.

Although there is linear relationship, **the resistance is not directly proportional to the temperature**, because the graph does not pass through the origin. Notice that the **thermistor has a resistance at 0°C**, so the graph touches the vertical axis.

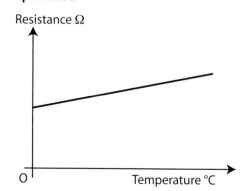

Candidates should be aware that they are required to perform, and **may** be asked to describe, experiments to conduct the current–voltage characteristics for a metallic conductor and a negative temperature coefficient (NTC) thermistor. This is the third of five references to experimental work within the AS 1 part of the specification.

By contrast, the **resistance of an NTC thermistor falls exponentially with temperature**, as shown:

Even at high temperatures a thermistor has a finite resistance, so the graph never touches the horizontal axis.

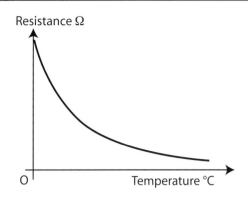

Resistivity

Experiment shows that the resistance of a metal conductor at a constant temperature is:
• **directly proportional** its length, L
• **inversely proportional** to its area of cross section, A
This information is represented graphically below.

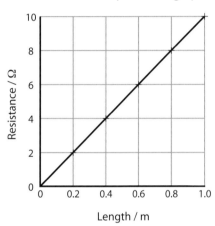 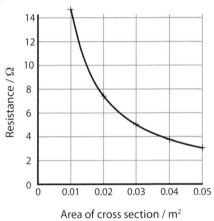 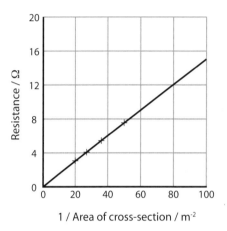

The resistance also depends on the material of the conductor. **Each material has a constant known as its resistivity** and is given the symbol, ρ (pronounced 'rho'). If we combine all these ideas, we have:

$$R = \frac{\rho l}{A}$$

where   R = resistance in Ω
A = area of cross section in m^2
L = length in m
ρ = resistivity in Ωm

The **resistivity of a material** is defined as **numerically equal to the resistance of a sample of the material 1 m long and of cross sectional area 1 m^2**.
• **Resistivity** is a property of a **material**, such as copper, aluminium, iron etc.
• **Resistance** is a property of a **particular specimen** of a material.
The resistivities of materials vary widely. Metals have resistivity of around 1×10^{-8} Ωm while good insulators have resistivity of around 1×10^{-23} Ωm.

Measuring resistivity experimentally

This is the fourth of five experiments prescribed by the AS 1 specification. It is important to do the experiment as part of your training in practical classes and to enable you to give a detailed description of the procedure for the theory examination. The resistance wire under investigation, which has been previously freed from bends and kinks, is laid along a metre stick and secured in position at each end by means of insulating tape.

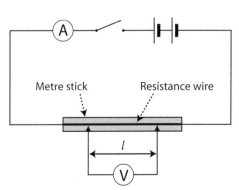

The electrical circuit is then set up as shown in the diagram above. Connections to the resistance wire are usually made using crocodile clips.

• The experiment involves measuring the voltage across different lengths of wire and the current passing through for lengths L ranging from about 20 cm to about 90 cm.

- From the voltage, V, and current, I, the resistance, R, can be found using $R = V \div I$.
- This is done at least twice per length of resistance wire to reduce the possibility of random error.
- Plot a graph of R against L. The graph will be a straight line through the origin.
- Now find the gradient of this line to determine the resistance per metre length of wire ($R \div L$).
- Using a micrometer screw gauge we now measure the diameter of the wire at about six points along its length.
- Determine the average diameter <d> and use $A = \pi<d>^2 / 4$ to find the wire's average cross section area, A.
- The last stage is to calculate the resistivity of the material of the wire, ρ.

$$\rho = \frac{RA}{L} = \frac{R.\pi\langle d\rangle^2}{4L} = \text{gradient of R} - \text{L graph} \times \frac{\pi\langle d\rangle^2}{4}$$

Worked Example

What length of resistance wire must be cut from a reel if the material has resistivity 1.57×10^{-8} Ωm, diameter 0.18 mm and is required to have a resistance as close as possible to 2.50 Ω?

Rearranging $R = \rho L \div A$ gives $L = RA \div \rho = R \times \pi d^2 \div 4\rho$

Hence $L = \{2.50 \times (0.18 \times 10^{-3})^2\} / (4 \times 1.57 \times 10^{-8}) = 4.05$ m

Worked Example

An electric hot plate consists of a 20 m length of manganin wire of resistivity of 4.4×10^{-7} Ωm and cross section area 0.23 mm². Calculate the power of the plate when connected to a 200 V electrical supply.

$P = IV = V^2 \div R = V^2A \div \rho L$
$= (200^2 \times 0.23 \times 10^{-6}) \div (4.4 \times 10^{-7} \times 20) = 1045$ W

Exercise 14

1. An electrician finds two coils of resistance wire in his bag. The coils of wire are made of materials of different electrical resistivity.
   (a) Define electrical resistivity.

   (b)(i) Coil A consists of wire 15 m long, with a diameter of 0.2 mm and a resistance of 9.0 Ω. Calculate the resistivity of the material of Coil A and state its unit.
   (ii) Coil B, consists of wire of the same length and diameter as the wire in Coil A but with a resistivity 30 times that of Coil A. Calculate the resistance of Coil B.

   (c) (i) The electrician has to fix two faults, a heating element and a break in the electrical circuit. He uses wire from the coils to mend the faults. Which coil of wire should the electrician select for each job?

   (ii) Explain your choice of wire to repair the heating element.
   (CCEA June 2010)

2. (a) A copper wire is 2.0 m long and has a radius of 0.56 mm. When the current in the wire is 3.5 A, the potential difference between the ends of the wire is 0.12V. Calculate the resistivity of copper.

   (b) This copper wire (wire A) is now replaced with a different copper wire (wire B) of length 2.0 m (the same as before) but of radius 0.28 mm (half the previous value). State how the resistance and resistivity of wire B compare with the values of the corresponding quantities for wire A. In each case, explain your reasoning.
   (CCEA January 2009)

Internal Resistance

Sources of e.m.f. (electromotive force), such as batteries and power packs, have themselves some resistance to the electric current that passes through them. This is called their **internal** resistance and it has two effects:

1. As more current is drawn from the battery or power pack, the voltage across the terminals of the supply falls.

2. The source of e.m.f. is less than 100% efficient as energy is dissipated as heat within it.

The e.m.f. is the **open-circuit voltage**. The internal resistance of a source of e.m.f. may be thought of as a **resistance r in series with the supply** as shown in the diagram,

where   E = e.m.f. of the cell in V
        V = voltage across the terminals in V
        r = internal resistance in Ω
        R = load resistance in Ω

Total resistance of circuit = R + r

Current $I = \dfrac{E}{R+r}$

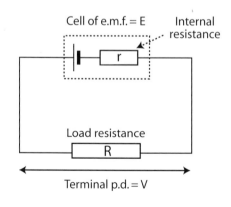

The p.d. across the load resistance is also the p.d. across the terminals of the cell and is known as the terminal potential difference V:

Terminal potential difference $V = IR$

The potential difference lost in the internal resistance is $v = Ir$, so: **$E = V + v = IR + Ir$**

The maximum current that can be taken from a power supply occurs when the cell is shortcircuited (so there is no load resistance, $R = 0$):

$$I_{max} = \frac{E}{r}$$

Internal Resistance and the Law of Conservation of Energy

Analysis of the circuit above shows that: $E = V + Ir$

If both sides of the equation are multiplied by I, the result is:

$$EI \quad = \quad VI \quad + \quad I^2r$$

| Power released by chemical energy in battery | Power delivered to the the external circuit | Power dissipated in the internal resistance of the battery |

This is simply an application of the law of conservation of energy to a battery with an internal resistance.

Worked Example

When a 12 V battery is short-circuited, the current drawn is 6 A. What current would you expect to flow when the load resistor is 4 Ω?

Internal resistance = $V \div I = 12 \div 6 = 2\,\Omega$.

When the load is 4 Ω, the total resistance is $2 + 4 = 6\,\Omega$, so $I = V \div R = 12 \div 6 = 2$ A.

Worked Example

Three identical cells each have an internal resistance of 0.5 Ω. They are connected in series with each other across a load resistor of 1.5 Ω. If the e.m.f. of each cell is 2.0 V, calculate the current drawn from the battery and the power dissipated in the load resistor.

I = battery voltage ÷ circuit resistance
= $(3 \times 2.0) \div (3 \times 0.5 + 1.5) = 2.0$ A

Power in external resistor = $I^2R = 2.0^2 \times 1.5 = 6.0$ W

Experiment to find the Internal Resistance of a Cell

Determination of the internal resistance of a cell is the last of the five experiments prescribed by the specification for AS 1. You should therefore be able to describe the experiment in detail.

The procedure is as follows:

* Using a 'D' cell (commonly called a torch battery) and a 5 Ω rheostat set to its highest resistance, assemble the circuit as shown below.

* Record the terminal voltage, V, and current, I, drawn from the cell.

* Reduce the load resistance slightly and record the new values of V and I.

* Repeat for different load resistances, R ranging from 5 Ω to zero.

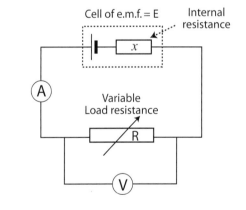

Theory

$E = I(r + R) = Ir + IR = Ir + V$

Rearranging gives $V = E - Ir$

Comparing this with $y = mx + c$ shows that a graph of V against I gives a straight line of slope $-r$ and y-axis intercept of E.

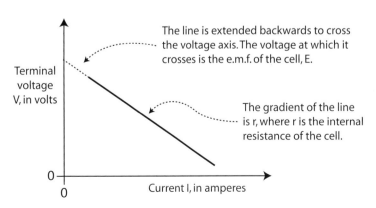

The line is extended backwards to cross the voltage axis. The voltage at which it crosses is the e.m.f. of the cell, E.

The gradient of the line is r, where r is the internal resistance of the cell.

Superconductivity

The electrical resistance of metals decreases as the temperature falls. For some materials, at a very low temperature, called the **transition temperature,** the resistivity (and hence the resistance) falls to zero. This phenomenon is called **superconductivity**.

The graph showing superconductivity in mercury is shown opposite.

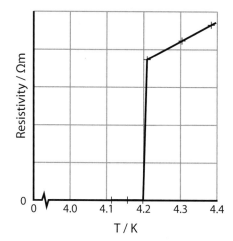

We can define a material as a superconductor if it loses all its electrical resistivity to become a perfect conductor when it is below its transition temperature.

Superconductors are used:
• to produce the strong magnetic fields needed for **(MRI) scanners**.
• in **Maglev (magnetic levitation) monorail systems**.

Exercise 15

1. A source of electromotive force has an internal resistance.
   (a) Describe an effect of this internal resistance.

   (b) An experiment is performed to determine the internal resistance r of a cell using the circuit below.

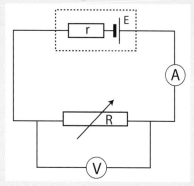

   By varying the load resistance, R, results were obtained for the terminal voltage V and the current drawn from the cell. A graph of the results was plotted and is shown below.

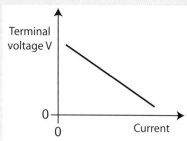

   (i) Explain how the internal resistance r may be obtained from the graph.

   (ii) Explain how the e.m.f. E of the cell may be obtained from the graph.

   (c) When no current is drawn from the cell, the p.d. between its terminals is 10.0 V. When a load resistor of 2.0 Ω is connected across the battery the p.d. between the terminals is 9.5 V. Calculate the internal resistance of the cell.
   (CCEA June 2010)

2. (a) Terms often used in describing an electrical power source, such as a battery, are terminal potential difference and electromotive force (e.m.f.). Write a short explanation of these terms and when it is appropriate to use them.

   (b) (i) What is meant by the internal resistance of an electrical power source?
   (ii) Describe an experiment to find the internal resistance of a battery. Include a circuit diagram. Show how a value of the internal resistance can be obtained from the series of experimental results. Show also how the e.m.f. of the battery can be obtained.
   (CCEA June 2009)

Students should be able to:

1.12.1 use conservation of charge and energy in simple d.c. circuits;

1.12.2 recall and use the equations for resistors in series and in parallel;

1.12.3 understand the use of a potential divider as a source of variable p.d.; and

1.12.4 use $V_{out} = \dfrac{R_1 V_{in}}{R_1 + R_2}$

Conservation of charge

A fundamental law of physics is that **electrical charge** is conserved. When a neutral plastic rod is charged by friction by rubbing it with a neutral duster, the rod and the duster obtain equal amounts of charge, but of the opposite sign. Their total charge is therefore zero, as it was at the beginning.

The sum of the charges entering a junction per second must therefore be equal to the sum of the charges leaving it per second, to be in agreement with the law of conservation of electric charge.

But current is the charge passing a fixed point per second, so
sum of currents entering junction = sum of currents leaving junction

or $\Sigma I_{in} = \Sigma I_{out}$

The mathematical symbol Σ (sigma) simply means 'the sum of'.

The statement above is called **Kirchhoff's First Law** or Kirchhoff's law of electric charge and is a direct consequence of the law of conservation of charge. Some students prefer to express the law as:
The algebraic sum of the currents at a junction is zero.

Worked Example

Suppose a current of 8 A flows into a junction and currents of 2 A and 1 A flow out of it as illustrated in the diagram. How much current, I, flows in the remaining fourth arm and in what direction does it flow?

Applying Kirchhoff's Law gives us:

$8 + (-2) + (-1) + I = 0$

So, $I = -5$ A.

This is interpreted as meaning the current I has a

magnitude of **5 A** and its direction is **out of the junction**.

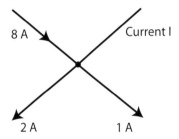

Worked Example

Use the data in the diagram to calculate the size and direction of the current in AB and BC.

Suppose the current in AB is I_1.
Then applying Kirchhoff's First Law at point A:
$I_1 - 4 - 1 = 0$, so $I_1 = 5$ A
i.e. a current of 5 A flows from B towards A.

Suppose the current in BC is I_2.
Then applying Kirchhoff's First Law at point B:
$I_2 + 2 - 5 = 0$, so $I_2 = 3$ A

i.e. a current of 3 A flows from C towards B.

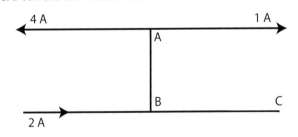

Conservation of Energy

When a current I flows from a cell of e.m.f. E, then every second cell produces an amount of electrical energy equal to the product IE. This energy is all dissipated in the external load resistor and the cell's internal resistance. By the Principle of Conservation of Energy we can write:

Electrical energy produced per second in cell		Heat energy produced per second internal resistance		Heat energy produced per second in in load resistance
IE	=	$I^2 r$	+	$I^2 R$

Worked Example

A cell of e.m.f. 12 V delivers a current of 2 A to an external load resistor of resistance 5 Ω. The load dissipates 20 J of heat energy per second. Find:
(a) the total electrical power produced by the cell;
(b) the power lost in the internal resistance;
(c) the resistance of the internal resistor.

(a) Power of cell = IE = 2 × 12 = 24 W
(b) Power lost = Power produced – Power in load
  = 24 – 20 = 4 W
(c) Power lost = I^2r, so 4 = 2^2r giving r = 1 Ω

Resistors in series and in parallel

Recall that in section 1.11 we established the rules for resistors in series and in parallel.

The total resistance of resistors R_T in a **series** network is given by:
$$R_T = R_1 + R_2 + R_3 + \ldots$$

The total resistance of resistors R_T in a **parallel** network is given by:
$$\frac{1}{R_T} = \frac{1}{R_1} + \frac{1}{R_2} + \frac{1}{R_3} + \ldots$$

When there are **just two resistors in parallel** the equation above for R_T reduces to:
$$R_T = \frac{R_1 \times R_2}{R_1 + R_2}$$

Worked Example

In the network below all the resistors have a resistance of 4 Ω. Find the total resistance between points:
(i) A and B (ii) B and C (iii) A and C (iv) B and D and (v) A and D

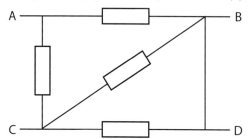

(i) The 4 Ω in CD is in parallel with the diagonal 4 Ω resistor between B and C and together these give 2 Ω. This 2 Ω combination is in series with the 4 Ω resistor in AC to

give 6 Ω. This 6 Ω is in parallel with the 4 Ω resistor in AB to give a total resistance of 2.4 Ω.

(ii) In BAC there is a total resistance of 8 Ω. BC therefore is a combination of 8 Ω, 4 Ω and 4 Ω, all in parallel with each other. This gives a total resistance of 1.6 Ω.

(iii) The 4 Ω in CD is in parallel with the diagonal 4 Ω resistor between B and C and together these give 2 Ω. This 2 Ω combination is in series with the 4 Ω resistor in BA to give 6 Ω. This 6 Ω is in parallel with the 4 Ω resistor in AC to give a total resistance of 2.4 Ω.

(iv) 0 Ω (The connecting wire short circuits the other parts of the network.)

(v) Points B and D are electrically identical. So the total resistance between AD is exactly the same as the total resistance between AB, which is 2.4 Ω.

Exercise 16

1. The diagram shows a heating element as used in the rear window of a car. It consists of six strips of resistive material, joined by strips of copper of negligible resistance. The voltage applied to the heater is 14.2 V when the engine is running. The total current delivered to the heater by the battery is 8.4 A.

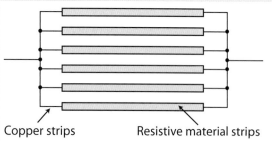

Copper strips   Resistive material strips

(a)(i) Calculate the total resistance of the element.
  (ii) Calculate the power delivered by the battery to the heating element.
(b)(i) Calculate the resistance of one of the strips of resistive material.

(c) The heating element has six strips connected in parallel. Suggest two reasons why this arrangement is preferable to connecting the same strips in series. (CCEA June 2009, part)

2. The diagram shows an arrangement of the resistors.

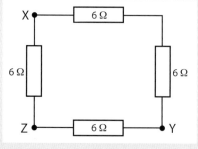

(i) Calculate the resistance between terminals X and Y.

(ii) An additional 6 Ω resistor is connected between terminals X and Y so that it is in parallel with both pairs of 6 Ω resistors. Calculate the total resistance between terminals Y and Z.
(CCEA June 2010, part)

Potential Divider

A potential divider is an arrangement of resistors which allows a fraction of the p.d. supplied to it to be passed on to an external circuit.

In the circuit shown the current, I in resistor R_1 is given by:

$$I = \frac{V_{in}}{R_1 + R_2}$$

The output voltage is the potential difference across R_1:

$$V_{OUT} = I \times R_1$$

Appling Ohm's Law to R_1:

$$V_{out} = \frac{R_1 V_{in}}{R_1 + R_2}$$

With fixed resistors, the potential divider **does not permit the user to vary the output voltage**. To do that the fixed resistors are replaced by a **rheostat**, as shown below. A rheostat used in this way is called a **potentiometer**. The output voltage is then continuously variable. The output voltage is then connected across a **load resistor**.

Note that **the output voltage is simply a fraction of the input voltage**. Students must understand that the fraction involved is the ratio of the resistance across which the output voltage is taken to the total resistance of the circuit.

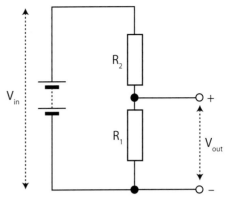

Potential divider with fixed resistors

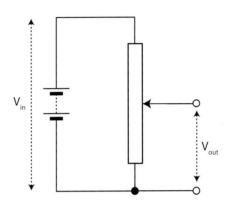

Potential divider with a rheostat

Worked Example

The circuit shows a potential divider.

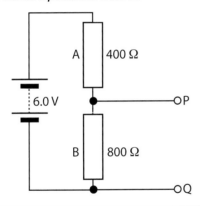

(i) What is the magnitude of the potential difference between the terminals P and Q?

(ii) A resistor of resistance 400 Ω is now connected in parallel with the 800 Ω. Calculate the new p.d. between P and Q.

(i) $V_{OUT} = V_{PQ} = \dfrac{R_1}{R_1 + R_2} \times V_{IN} = \dfrac{800}{1200} \times 6 = 4.0\,V$

(ii) The combined resistance of the resistors in parallel is

$$R_T = \frac{R_1 \times R_2}{R_1 + R_2} = (800 \times 400) \div (800 + 400) = 266.67\,\Omega$$

$$V_{OUT} = V_{PQ} = \frac{R_1}{R_1 + R_2} \times V_{IN} = \frac{266.67}{(266.67 + 400)} \times 6.0 = 2.4\,V$$

Effect of loading on V_{OUT}

In the worked example, the addition of the 400 Ω across the terminals P and Q has reduced the maximum output voltage of the potential divider from 4.0 V to 2.4 V. In general, **the voltage across the load decreases as the resistance of the load decreases**. Note that:

• Where there is infinite load, resistance V_{OUT} is a maximum.

• If there is zero load, resistance, V_{OUT} is zero.

Exercise 17

1. The diagram overleaf shows two fixed resistors and a variable resistor connected in series to an 18 V battery of negligible internal resistance. The arrangement gives a variable output voltage between C and D.

   (i) Calculate the current in the circuit.
   (ii) Hence calculate the potential difference across the

120 Ω variable resistor (the voltage between A and B).
(iii) Calculate the PD between the point D and the slider contact of the variable resistor (labelled C) when it is mid-way between A and B.
(iv) A 210 Ω resistor is now placed across the output between C and D. Calculate the new PD between C and D.

(CCEA January 2011)

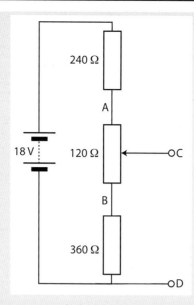

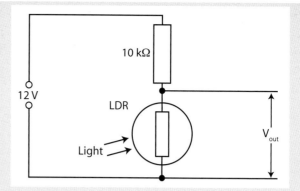

2. A circuit to turn on a light automatically when it gets dark is shown opposite. It makes use of a light dependent resistor, LDR, the resistance of which depends on the amount of light shining on it and a fixed resistor of resistance 10 kΩ.

(a) The LDR has a resistance of 500 Ω in bright light and 200 kΩ when it is dark.

(i) Calculate the output voltage V_{out}, when the LDR is in bright light.

(ii) The lamp connected across the output, V_{out} lights when V_{out} is greater than 10 V. Show that the lamp will light in the dark.

(b) Describe and explain what effect swapping the positions of the LDR and the fixed resistor in the circuit would have.

(CCEA January 2010)

Unit AS 2:
Waves, Photons and Medical Physics

2.1 Waves

Students should be able to:

2.1.1 demonstrate a knowledge and understanding of the terms 'transverse wave' and 'longitudinal wave';

2.1.2 be able to categorise waves as transverse or longitudinal;

2.1.3 understand polarisation as a phenomenon associated with transverse waves;

2.1.4 recall and use $v = f\lambda$;

2.1.5 recall radio waves, microwaves, infrared, visible, ultraviolet, x-rays and gamma-rays as regions of the electromagnetic spectrum;

2.1.6 state typical wavelengths for each of these regions;

2.1.7 analyse graphs to obtain data on amplitude, period, frequency, wavelength and phase;

Transverse and Longitudinal Waves

Waves are created by a disturbance which results in a vibration. A wave that transports energy by causing vibrations in the material or medium through which it moves is called a progressive wave.

In a **transverse wave** the vibrations are perpendicular to the direction in which the wave travels (ie carries energy or propagates).

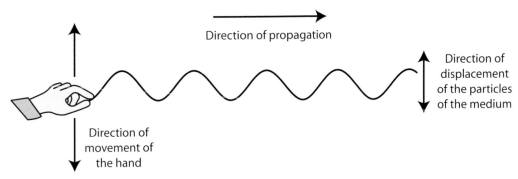

In a **longitudinal wave** the vibrations are parallel to the direction of propagation.

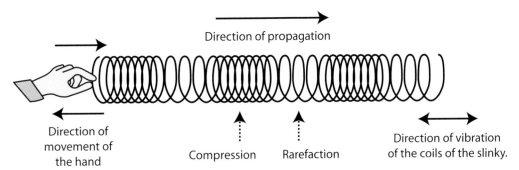

Polarisation

An electromagnetic wave is a transverse wave which has both an electric and a magnetic oscillating component. A light wave which is vibrating in more than one plane is referred to as unpolarised light.

Polarised light waves are light waves in which the vibrations occur in a single plane. The process of transforming unpolarised light into polarised light is known as polarisation and can be achieved using a polarising filter.

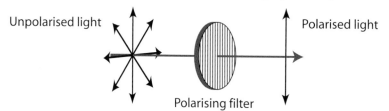

When you view the polarised light through a second polarising filter (analyser) the intensity of the transmitted light falls to a minimum after the analyser has been rotated through 90°. A further rotation of 90° will see the transmitted light intensity reach a maximum again.

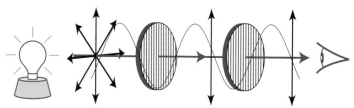

Definitions

The **period** of a wave is the time for a particle on a medium to make one complete cycle.

The **frequency** is the number of complete waves that pass a point in one second. Frequency is measured in hertz, (Hz). A frequency of 100 Hz means 100 waves per second pass a point or the particle of the medium completes 100 oscillations in one second.

The **wavelength** is defined as the distance the wave form progresses in the periodic time, T. The wavelength can be measured as the distance from crest to next crest, or from trough to next trough.

The **amplitude** of a wave is the maximum displacement of a particle of the medium from its rest position.

Velocity of the Wave

The velocity of the wave can be calculated from its wavelength and frequency using the following equation:

$$v = f\lambda$$

where
v = velocity in ms^{-1}
f = frequency in Hz
λ = wavelength in m

Spectrum of Electromagnetic Waves

Electromagnetic waves exist with a very large range of wavelengths. This continuous range of wavelengths is known as the electromagnetic spectrum:

Wave	Gamma	X ray	Ultraviolet	Visible	Infrared	Microwave	Radio
Wavelength/m	10^{-11}	10^{-9}	10^{-7}	Violet $= 4 \times 10^{-7}$ Red $= 7 \times 10^{-7}$	10^{-4}	10^{-2}	10
Frequency/Hz	10^{19}	10^{18}	10^{16}	Violet $= 7 \times 10^{14}$ Red $= 4 \times 10^{14}$	10^{13}	10^{10}	10^{8}

Graphical Representation of a Wave

Both transverse and longitudinal waves can be represented graphically in two ways:

1. Displacement of a particle of the medium against time.

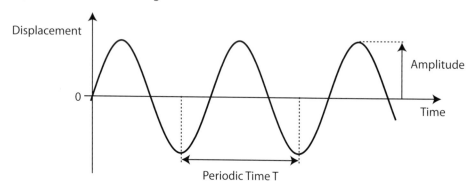

2. Displacement of the particles of the medium against distance along the wave.

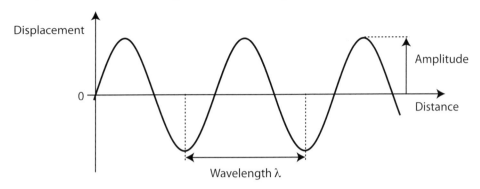

Phase

If two particles are vibrating so that at the same instant they are at the same distance and same direction (same displacement) from their equilibrium positions they are said to be in phase.

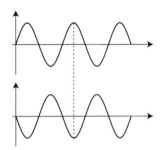

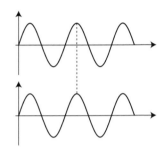

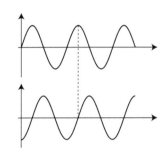

These two waves are out of phase. The crests of one exactly coincide with the troughs of the other. Their phase difference is ½ λ.

These two waves are in phase. The crests of one exactly coincide with the crests of the other.

These two waves are out of phase. The crests of one exactly coincide with the point where the displacement of the other wave is zero. Their phase difference is ¼ λ.

Worked Example

The graphs of displacement against time for two waves A and B are shown opposite.

(a) (i) State the amplitude of A.
  (ii) Calculate the frequency of wave A.

(b) Are the graphs shown useful in classifying the waves as transverse? Explain your answer.

(c) (i) Waves A and B are not in phase. Explain what is meant by phase.
  (ii) What is the phase difference between wave A and wave B?

(CCEA January 2010)

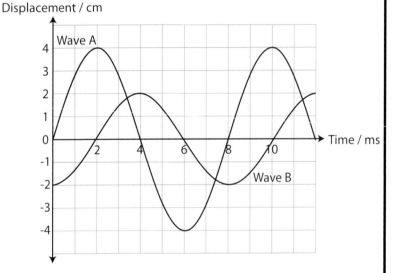

(a) (i) The amplitude is the maximum displacement of produced by the wave. Unlike the displacement it is not a vector so + or – is not required. Reading from the graph, making sure you note the scale on the vertical axis, it is 4 cm.
  (ii) The frequency = 1/period. The horizontal axis will give the time for one complete wave. Reading from the graph, noting the scale is in ms (milliseconds, 10^{-3}s), gives 8 ms or 8×10^{-3} Frequency = $1 \div 8 \times 10^{-3}$ = 125 Hz

(b) No. Although the graph shows displacement against time it does not show if the vibrations are perpendicular to the direction of propagation of the wave (transverse) or parallel to the direction of propagation (longitudinal).

(c) (i) Corresponding points on each wave coincide in time. Or one wave reaches its maximum positive displacement at the same time as the other wave also reaches its maximum positive displacement.
  (ii) Wave A reaches its maximum positive displacement 2 divisions before wave B reaches its maximum positive displacement. 2 divisions = 2 ms. This is ¼ of the period, so the phase difference is ¼ T or ¼ wave = ¼ of 360° = 90° or ¼ of 2π = π/2 radians.

Worked Example

Light from a lamp is unpolarised.
(a) Explain what is meant by unpolarised.
(b) Give an example of a wave that cannot be polarised and explain why it cannot be polarised.
(CCEA January 2011)

(a) The vibrations take in all planes, or, the plane in which the vibrations take place is continuously changing.

(b) Sound. Sound is a longitudinal wave and the vibrations occur parallel to the direction in which the wave is propagating. Hence it cannot be polarised.

Worked Example

(a) State a typical wavelength for visible light.

(b) An electromagnetic wave from a different region of the electromagnetic spectrum has frequency of 620 GHz. What is its wavelength of it is travelling in a vacuum?
(CCEA June 2009)

(a) Visible light has wavelengths from 400 nm (4×10^{-7} m) (violet) to 600 nm (6×10^{-7} m) (red).

(b) Use the wave equation $v = f\lambda$.
$f = 620$ GHz $= 620 \times 10^9$ Hz.
$v = 3 \times 10^8$ ms^{-1} (from data sheet)
Re-arranging gives $\lambda = 3 \times 10^8 \div 620 \times 10^9 = 4.84 \times 10^{-4}$ m

Exercise 18

1. (a)(i) A beam of light is polarised. Explain the meaning of the term polarised.
   (ii) Describe how you would confirm that a beam of light is polarised.
   (iii) Sound waves are longitudinal. Explain why these waves cannot be polarised.

   (b) A loudspeaker at an open air music festival vibrates at a frequency of 512 Hz. The sound emitted by the loudspeaker takes 0.510 s to reach a person who is standing 170 m from the loudspeaker. Calculate the wavelength of the sound emitted by the loudspeaker.
   (CCEA June 2010)

2. (a) A wave of fixed velocity passes along a stretched string. The diagram below shows a graph of the displacement d of a particle of the string against time t.

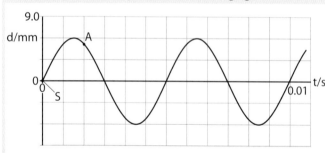

   (i) Describe the direction of the particle's displacement relative to the velocity of the wave. Hence state the type of wave.
   (ii) Determine the amplitude of the wave.
   (iii) Determine the frequency of the wave.
   (iv) The velocity of the wave is 890.0 mms^{-1}. Calculate the wavelength of the wave.

   (b) Calculate the phase difference and give its unit, between the point A on the diagram and the origin S.
   (CCEA January 2009)

3. The graphs below describe particle oscillation for the same wave.

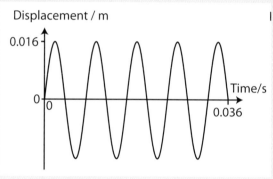

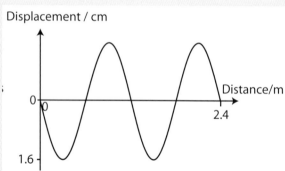

   (a) What evidence exists to support the claim that both graphs describe the same wave?
   (b) For the wave represented by the graphs above calculate;
       (i) the wavelength
       (ii) the frequency
       (iii) the speed
   (CCEA June 2011)

2.2 Refraction

Students should be able to:

2.2.1 describe an experiment to verify Snell's law;

2.2.2 recall and use the formula $\dfrac{\sin i}{\sin r} = n$;

2.2.3 perform and describe an experiment to measure refractive index;

2.2.4 demonstrate knowledge and understanding of total internal reflection; and

2.2.5 recall and use the formula $\sin C = \dfrac{1}{n}$;

Snell's Law

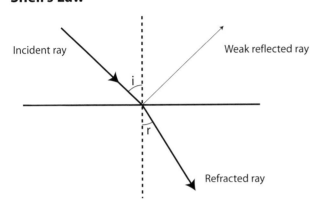

Refraction occurs when a wave, for example light, travels from one medium to another, for example from air into glass. Its direction of travel is changed. The angle between the incident ray and the normal is called the angle of incidence **i**. The angle between the normal and the refracted ray is called the angle of refraction **r**. Note that the angles are measured from the normal.

Snell's Law states: For light travelling from one material to another, the ratio is a constant known as the refractive index:

$$\text{refractive index of a material} = \frac{\text{speed of light in a vacuum}}{\text{speed of light in the material}}$$

The refractive index **n** can also be calculated by the formula:

$$n = \frac{\sin i}{\sin r}$$

Experimental Verification of Snell's Law and Measurement of Refractive Index

This is one of the experiments prescribed by CCEA Specification for AS 2. It can be done by ray tracing through a glass block. Place the glass block on a sheet of paper and carefully trace around it. Remove the glass block and mark the normal at one edge and extend this line into the position of the glass block. Replace the glass block.

Remove the glass block, join up the crosses to show the incident, refracted and emergent rays. Using a protractor measure the angles of incidence and refraction. Carefully replace the glass block and repeat this procedure for a number of incident rays with angles of incidence.

When sin i is plotted against sin r, the result is a straight line through the origin, verifying Snell's Law. The gradient of the line gives the value for the refractive index.

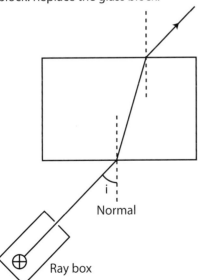

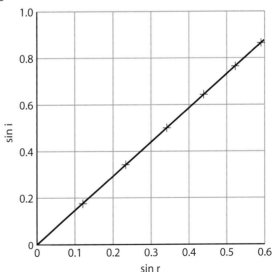

A ray box is used to produce a narrow ray. Shine the ray into the block so that it meet the block at the point where the normal meets the block. Mark this path carefully with crosses. Mark the emergent ray in a similar fashion.

Critical Angle

When light travels from a material of high refractive index to one of lower refractive index, for example from glass into air, it is bent away from the normal. The angle of incidence in the glass that produces this angle of refraction of 90° is called the **critical angle C**. Note that there is still a weak reflected ray.

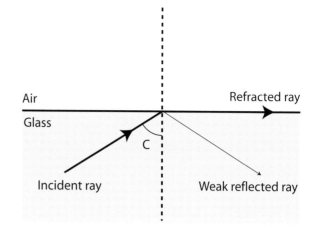

The relationship between the critical angle and the refractive index of the material can be derived by applying Snell's Law:

Since the refacted ray is at 90° to the normal

$$_{glass}n_{air} = \frac{\sin C}{\sin 90} = \sin C$$

Since $_{glass}n_{air} = \dfrac{1}{_{air}n_{glass}}$, therefore $\sin C = \dfrac{1}{_{air}n_{glass}}$

Total Internal Reflection

When the angle of incidence in the material with the higher refractive index is greater than the critical angle, a phenomenon known as **total internal reflection** occurs. Total internal reflection involves the reflection of all the incident light at the boundary between two materials.

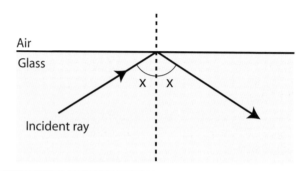

Worked Example

The diagram shows the outline ABCD of a rectangular block made of glass of refractive index 1.46. A ray of light is incident at an angle of incidence of 75.0o on side AB. The angle of refraction for this ray is 41.4°. The refracted ray meets face AD.

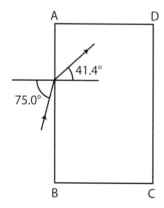

(a) Calculate the angle of incidence of this ray when it meets face AD.
(b) Calculate the critical angle for a ray in this glass meeting the glass/air boundary.
(c) Use your answers to deduce what will happen to the ray
when it meets face AD.
(d) On the diagram continue the path of the ray until it has left the glass block.
(CCEA January 2010)

(a) From the geometry (see diagram) the angle is 90° – 41.4°
= 48.6°.

(b) sin c = 1÷n = 1÷1.46 = 0.6849 giving c = 43.2°.

(c) The ray makes an angle of incidence of 48.6° with the side AD. This angle is greater than the critical angle resulting in total internal reflection at AD. The ray then meets the other side of the block at an angle of incidence of 41.4° and ray emerges into the air making an angle of refraction of 75°.

(d)

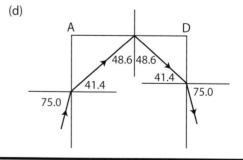

Exercise 19

1. In an experiment to measure the refractive index of glass, a series of results for a range of angles of incidence and their corresponding angles of refraction has been obtained. Describe how these results may be processed to obtain an accurate value for the refractive index of glass.
(CCEA June 2010]

2. A ray of light enters a medium of refractive index 1.39 at an angle as shown opposite. The ray is refracted inside the medium and travels to the upper surface where it is incident at the critical angle.

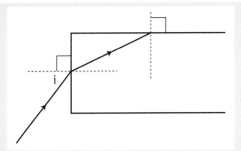

(a) Describe what happens to the ray at the upper surface.

(b) What would occur if another ray met the upper surface at an angle greater than the critical angle?

(c) Calculate the critical angle of the medium.

(d) Calculate the magnitude of the incident angle.

(CCEA January 2009)

3. A ray of light travels from inside a block of transparent material to air. The refractive index of the material of the block is 1.38. The ray emerges from the block into the air at angle of 43.0° to the normal. Calculate the minimum increase in the angle of the ray inside the block, to cause the ray to undergo total internal reflection.

(CCEA June 2010)

4. A short pulse of light enters a straight optical fibre of length 1.20 km. The pulse travels along the axis of the fibre as shown below.

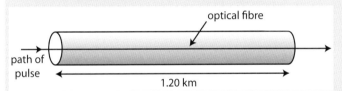

(a) The pulse takes 5880 ns to pass along the fibre. Calculate the velocity of light in the material of the fibre.

(b) Calculate the refractive index of the material.

(c) Calculate the critical angle of the material.

(CCEA January 2009)

5. The diagram shows a prism, made of glass of refractive index 1.52. Each of the angles of the prism is 60.0°. A ray of light strikes the face AB at point P at an angle of incidence of 45.0°. After refraction at P, the ray crosses the prism to Q, where it is refracted out of the prism.

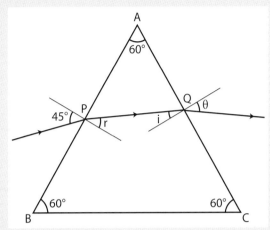

(a) Calculate the angle of refraction r of the ray after it enters the prism at P.

(b) The refracted ray crosses the prism, striking face AC at Q. Calculate the angle of incidence i of this ray on face AC. Hint: angle r + angle i = the angle of the prism.

(c) One of the conditions for total internal reflection is **not** satisfied when the ray meets face AC, so that the ray **does** emerge from the prism. State which condition is **not** met and support this with appropriate calculations.

(d) Calculate the angle θ to the normal at which the ray emerges from the prism.

(CCEA January 2008)

2.3 Lenses

Students should be able to:

2.3.1 draw ray diagrams for converging and diverging lenses;

2.3.2 use the equation $\dfrac{1}{u}+\dfrac{1}{v}=\dfrac{1}{f}$ for converging lenses;

2.3.3 perform and describe an experiment to measure the focal length of a converging lens;

2.3.4 recall and use the equation $m=\dfrac{v}{u}$;

2.3.5 describe the use of lenses to correct myopia and hypermetropia;

2.3.6 perform calculations on the correction of long sight;

2.3.7 perform calculations involving the lens power of converging lenses;

Types of Lenses

Lenses can be classified into converging (convex) and diverging (concave). These two types of lens have a different effect on a parallel beam of light.

When parallel rays of light pass through a **converging** lens they are refracted so that they pass through the focal point or principal focus of the lens. This type of principal focus is described as **real**.

Converging or convex lens

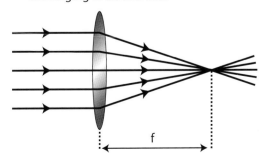

A **diverging** lens refracts the parallel rays so that they to spread out (diverge) from the focal point or principal focus of the concave lens. This type of principal focus is described as **virtual**.

The distance from the centre of a lens to the focal point is the focal length f.

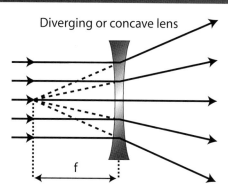

Diverging or concave lens

Ray Diagrams

The diagram below shows what happens to three particular rays when they pass through a **convex** lens.

To find the position, size and nature of the image formed by a convex lens we need to find where at least two rays of light meet (real image) or appear to meet (virtual image) having passed through the lens from the from the object.

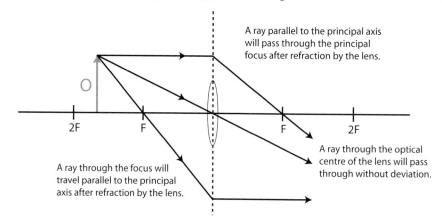

A ray parallel to the principal axis will pass through the principal focus after refraction by the lens.

A ray through the optical centre of the lens will pass through without deviation.

A ray through the focus will travel parallel to the principal axis after refraction by the lens.

The diagram below shows what happens to two particular rays when they pass through a **concave** lens. Regardless of the position of the object, the image formed is always virtual, erect and diminished. To locate the image we need to find the point where the two rays appear to meet (virtual image).

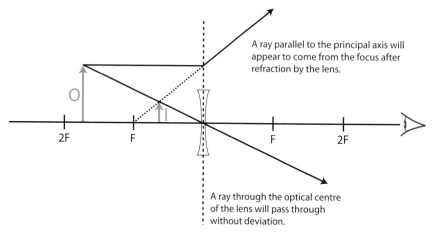

A ray parallel to the principal axis will appear to come from the focus after refraction by the lens.

A ray through the optical centre of the lens will pass through without deviation.

Measurement of Focal Length (Converging lens)

This is one of the experiments prescribed by the CCEA specifcation for AS 2. Particular attention should be payed to the Plane Mirror Method and the Measuring Object and Image Distances Method.

Approximate Method

Light from a distant object, more than 10 m away, is approximately parallel. Adjust the distance from the lens to the screen so that image is as sharp as possible. Measure this distance; it is approximately the focal length. This should be repeated a number of times and take the average.

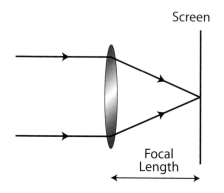

Screen

Focal Length

Plane Mirror Method

Place the plane mirror as close as possible to the lens. Move the lens and plane mirror together until a sharp image of the wire mesh appears on the front of the lamp house. Measure the distance from the lens to the lamp house, this is the focal length of the lens. Repetition and the taking of an average improves the reliability of the result.

Measuring Object and Image Distances

Measure the distance from the mesh to the lens; this is the object distance u. The position of the screen is adjusted until a sharp image is produced on the screen. The lens formula can then be used to calculate the focal length:

$$\frac{1}{u}+\frac{1}{v}=\frac{1}{f}$$

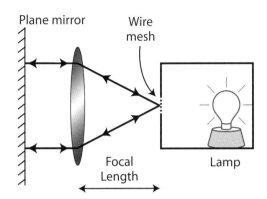

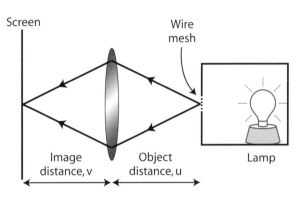

The better approach is to obtain a series of values of u and v and use your results to plot a linear graph. This is achieved by plotting 1/u against 1/v. This yields a straight line as shown on the right. The intercept on each axes provides a value for 1/f.

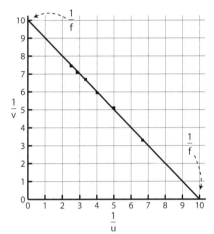

Magnification

The linear magnification m of an image is the size of the image divided by the size of the object. By using the properties of similar triangles we can also show that magnification is also equal to the ratio of the image distance to the object distance:

$$m=\frac{v}{u}$$

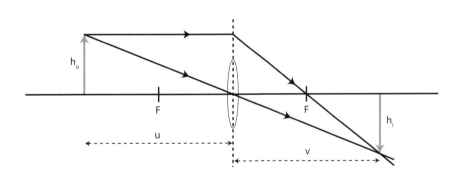

Power of a Lens

The power of lens is defined as $\frac{1}{f}$

where   focal length is measured in metres
power is measured in m^{-1} or dioptres, symbol D.

A diverging lens has a negative power, a converging lens has a positive power.

Real/Virtual Sign Convention

The distance to a real image is positive. The distance to a virtual image is negative.
A convex lens has a positive focal length. A concave lens has a negative focal length.

Exercise 20

1. An object labelled O is placed in front of a diverging lens L as shown. Copy and complete the ray diagram to locate the position if the image obtained. Label the image I. The principal axis of the lens and the ray incident on the optical centre of the lens are included in the diagram. The locations of the principal foci are marked F_1 and F_2.
(CCEA June 2011)

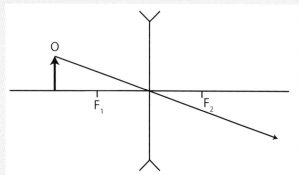

2. Describe an experiment to determine the focal length of a converging lens. Your description should include
(a) a fully labelled diagram of the apparatus you intend to use,
(b) an outline of the method employed,
(c) the results to be taken,
(d) an analysis of how the results can be used to obtain a value for the focal length of the converging lens.

The quality of written communication was assessed in this question.
(CCEA January 2010)

3. The focal length of a converging lens used to form a virtual and magnified image is 10.0 cm.
(a) Calculate how far away from the lens an object must be placed in order to form a virtual image which is six times larger than the object.
(b) Calculate how far from the lens this image is formed.
(CCEA June 2008)

Myopia and Hypermetropia

The ability of the eye to see objects clearly at different distances is known as **accommodation**.

The farthest point which can be seen clearly by the unaided eye is called the **far point**. For the normal eye this is at infinity. Light from the far point reaches the eye as parallel rays. The rays are refracted by the eye so that they meet on the retina forming a sharp image of the distant object.

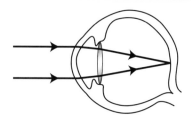

The nearest point which can be seen clearly by the unaided eye is called the **near point**. For the normal eye this is at 25 cm. The light from the near point reaches the eye as diverging rays. These are refracted by the eye so that they meet on the retina forming a sharp image of the object at the near point.

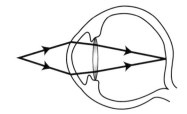

Myopia (Short Sight)

A person who suffers from myopia (short sight) is unable to see distant objects sharply. This causes the light from distant objects to converge towards a point in front of the retina. The person's far point is much closer to the eye than the normal infinite distance.

To correct this defect a concave (diverging) lens is used. **The focal length of the lens is equal to the distance to the person's actual far point.** This means that parallel rays of light from a distant object are refracted so that they appear to diverge from the person's far point.

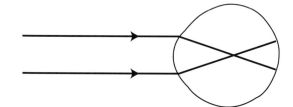

Hypermetropia (Long Sight)

A long sighted person sees distant objects clearly but does not see near objects clearly. An object held at the normal near point distance of 25 cm will not be seen clearly. The rays of light from the object are not bent sufficiently to form an image on the retina.

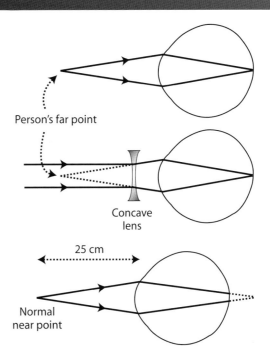

Person's far point

Concave lens

The near point is much further than 25 cm. Rays of light from an object placed at their near point are bent so that they meet on the retina resulting in the object being seen clearly. To correct for this defect a convex lens is used. **The focal length of this lens has to be such that an object at 25 cm appears to be at the person's near point.**

25 cm

Normal near point

Worked Example

A person has a near point at 100 cm. Calculate the focal length and the power of the lens needed to correct this defect.

The convex lens has to create a **virtual image** at 100 cm of an object at 25 cm. Because the image at the person's near point is virtual, we use a negative sign.

If the person's near point is 100 cm from his eye then:

$$\frac{1}{u}+\frac{1}{v}=\frac{1}{f} \qquad \frac{1}{25}+\frac{1}{(-100)}=\frac{1}{f} \text{ so } \frac{1}{f}=\frac{3}{100}$$

giving f = 33.3 cm (0.333 m)

$$\text{or a power} = \frac{1}{0.333} = +3.0 \text{ D}$$

The convex lens needed has a focal length of 33.3 (0.333 m) and a power of +3.0 D

Exercise 21

1. When an object is placed 32 cm in front of a converging lens a virtual image is formed. The image is 2.7 times larger than the object. This is the magnification of the lens which is defined by the equation;
   (a) State the defect of vision that this lens could be used to correct in the human eye.
   (b) (i) Calculate the power of the lens and state the unit of power.
       (ii) A person's near point when using this lens is 25 cm from the eye. What distance from the eye is the person's near point when unaided by this lens?
   (CCEA January 2011)

2. The diagram illustrates a defect of vision for a person's eye. The eye structure has been simplified. The eye is the circle and all the bending occurs at its left hand surface and the retina is the right hand surface of the circle. Two rays from a distant object are shown undergoing refraction at the eye.

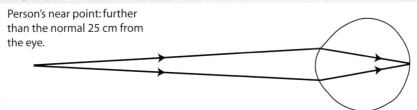

Person's near point: further than the normal 25 cm from the eye.

Name the eye defect illustrated and the type of lens that will correct this defect. (CCEA June 2009)

2.4 Superposition and Interference

Students should be able to:

2.4.1 illustrate the concept of superposition by the graphical addition of two sinusoidal waves;

2.4.2 demonstrate knowledge and understanding of the graphical representation of standing waves in stretched strings and air in pipes closed at one end;

2.4.3 identify node and anti-node positions;

2.4.4 understand the significance of coherence as applied to wave sources;

2.4.5 state the conditions for observable interference;

2.4.6 understand the significance of path difference and phase difference in explaining interference effects;

2.4.7 describe Young's slits interference experiment with monochromatic light; and

2.4.8 use the formula $\lambda = \dfrac{ay}{d}$ applied to Young's slits experiment.

Concept of Superposition

The Principle of Superposition states that the resultant displacement of the medium at any point in space, is the _vector_ sum of the displacements that each wave would cause at that point at that time.

When the two waves overlap in phase they produce a wave of greater amplitude. This is known as **constructive interference**. The crests of each wave coincide exactly (as do the troughs) and so a wave with greater amplitude is produced.

When the crest of one wave coincides with the trough of the other wave the displacements of the two waves are in opposite directions. If the amplitudes are equal then they cancel each other. This is called total **destructive interference**.

If the amplitudes are not the same then when destructive interference takes place the resultant wave has a smaller amplitude.

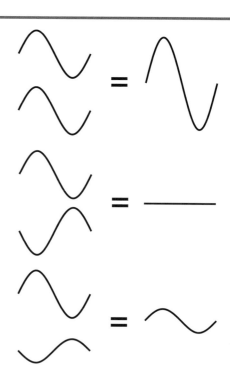

Coherence

To produce an interference pattern that is detectable, ie lasts long enough to seen or heard, the two sources of waves must be **coherent**.

To be coherent the sources must produce waves of the same wavelength or frequency and be in phase, ie each produces a wave crest at the same time, or have a constant phase difference between them.

To make the difference between constructive and destructive more obvious, it is best that the coherent sources are of equal amplitude.

Interference of Sound Waves

In the diagram, S1 and S2 are two speakers. To achieve coherent sources of sound, the same signal generator powers each speaker, so that they produce sound waves of the same frequency and in phase. As the sound waves from each speaker spread out they cross. This creates places where the sound is loud (constructive interference) and between these there are places where the sound is soft (destructive interference).

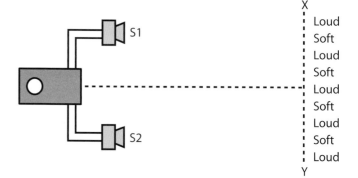

Interference of Light Waves - Young's Double Slit Experiment

In this experiment, light from a laser is allowed to illuminate two narrow slits, as shown in the diagram. Laser light is coherent.

Each slit then acts as a coherent source of light waves. As the waves spread out interference is observed on a screen a distance (1 to 2 metres) away. The bright fringes are due to constructive interference and dark ones dues to destructive interference.

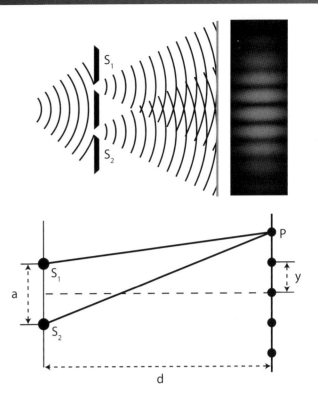

The diagram opposite shows the geometry of the two source interference experiment. S_1 and S_2 are two coherent sources of light, of wavelength λ, separated by a distance a. An interference pattern of alternate bright and dark fringes is seen on the screen. The separation of bright fringes is y.

The distance from the double slit to the screen is d. The point P is the location of a bright fringe. The waves reaching P from S_1 and S_2 have travelled different distances. If a whole number of wavelengths can fit into this path difference then constructive interference results since a crest from S_1 will arrive at the same time as a crest from S_2.

For constructive interference:

Path difference $S_2P - S_1P = n\lambda$ where n = 0, 1, 2, 3...

If a whole number of wavelengths plus ½ a wavelength can fit into this path difference then constructive interference results since a crest from S_1 will arrive at the same time as a trough from S_2.

For destructive interference:

Path difference $S_2P - S_1P = (n + \frac{1}{2})\lambda$ where n = 0, 1, 2, 3...

The wavelength can then be calculated using the formula

$$\lambda = \frac{ay}{d}$$

where λ = wavelength in m
a = separation of the two slits in m
y = separation of bright fringes in m
d = distance to the screen in m

Worked Example

(a) Laser light is monochromatic. What is meant by monochromatic?

(b) The diagram is a sketch of an arrangement used to measure the wavelength of light from a laser (not to scale).

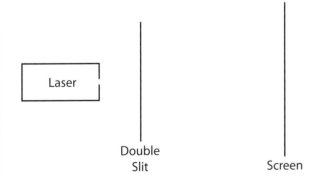

(i) Describe the pattern that will be seen on the screen.
(ii) The distance from the slits to the screen is 2.80 m. The centres of the slits are 0.24 mm apart. If the distance between the position of one maximum intensity and the next is 7.4 mm, calculate the wavelength of the laser light. Give your answer in nm.
(iii) State two ways in which the arrangement could be

changed, using the same laser, so that the distance between the positions of maximum intensity seen on the screen would be increased.
(CCEA January 2011)

(a) Monochromatic could be described as one colour. A much more precise answer and one that is more likely to achieve full marks, is to describe it as light of a single wavelength or frequency.

(b) (i) The pattern on the screen consists of a series of alternate bright and dark bands or fringes.

(ii) The wavelength can be calculated using $\lambda = \frac{ay}{d}$
$= (0.24 \times 10^{-3} \times 7.4 \times 10^{-3}) \div 2.80$
$= 6.34 \times 10^{-7}$ m
Note that all distances are converted to metres. Thus wavelength in namometres is 6340 nm

(iii) Re-arranging the equation gives $y = \frac{\lambda d}{a}$
The distance y can be increased by increasing d, ie increasing the distance from the double slits to the screen. It can also be increased by reducing the value of a, ie by making the two slits closer together.

Exercise 22

1. The diagram opposite illustrates an arrangement to observe interference. Laser light is incident upon an opaque slid on which two there are two transparent slits (labelled S and T). The light transmitted through these slits is initially in phase and overlaps in the region between the slits and the screen and the resulting interference pattern is observed on the screen.

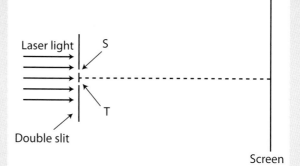

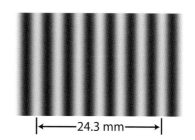

|←————24.3 mm————→|

(a) This arrangement ensures that the light emerging from the slits S and T is coherent. Explain the meaning of the term coherent in this context.

(b) With this arrangement light emerging from S and T is in phase. Explain the meaning of the term in phase in this context.

(c) The interference pattern obtained on the screen is a sequence of bright and dark bands as shown opposite. By considering the paths followed by the light from slits S and T, explain the formation of a bright interference fringe.

(d) On the interference pattern obtained, the distance between the centres of the seven bright fringes 24.3 mm (see the diagram). The laser light has a wavelength of 6.42×10^{-7} m and the separation of the double slits S and T is 0.66 mm. Use the data to determine the distance between the double slits and the screen.
(CCEA June 2011)

2. In a Young's slit interference experiment light of wavelength 550 nm is used. The separation of the slits is 0.910 mm and the central bright fringe of the pattern obtained is 1.80 m from the slits. At what distance from the central bright fringe of the pattern would the next bright fringe appear?
(CCEA June 2010)

3. (a) Explain the meaning of the term interference.
(b) What essential conditions must exist for an interference pattern?
(c) In Young's double slit experiment to show the interference of light what condition must also exist to produce good contrast between the bright and dark fringes in the interference pattern?
(CCEA January 2010)

Standing Waves in Stretched Strings

These are a produced by the interference of two waves, of the same type and having the same wavelength moving in opposite directions. The most common occurrence of this is a wave travelling in one direction meeting its reflection which is moving in the opposite direction. The ratio of the frequencies is therefore 1, 2 ,3 etc.

Fundamental frequency $= f_0$ and $\lambda_0 = 2L$
The velocity of the wave in the string $= v$

$$v = f_0 \lambda_0 \qquad f_0 = \frac{v}{\lambda_0} = \frac{v}{2L}$$

First overtone frequency $= f_1$ and $\lambda_1 = L$
The velocity of the wave in the string $= v$

$$v = f_1 \lambda_1 \qquad f_1 = \frac{v}{\lambda_1} = \frac{v}{L} = 2f_0$$

Second overtone frequency $= f_2$ and $\lambda_2 = \frac{2}{3}L$
The velocity of the wave in the string $= v$

$$v = f_2 \lambda_2 \qquad f_2 = \frac{v}{\lambda_2} = \frac{3v}{2L} = 3f_0$$

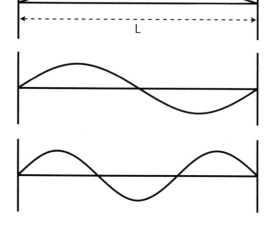

Nodes and Anti-Nodes

When a standing or stationary wave is created, some points along the wave are always at rest, their resultant displacement is always zero. These points are known as **nodes**.

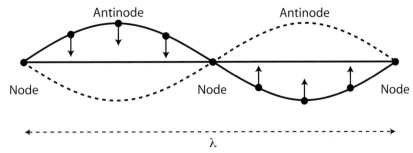

Between the nodes all the points are vibrating; the amplitude of vibration varies. Midway between the nodal points the amplitude of vibration is a maximum. This point is called an **anti-node**.

Exercise 23

1. The graphical representation of a standing wave on a stretched string is shown below.

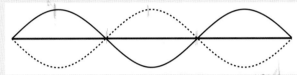

(a) Which mode of vibration is represented?

(b) Copy the diagram and mark clearly with the letter A one antinode.

(c) The distance between two consecutive antinodes in 0.08 m. What is the wavelength of the standing wave?

(d) Draw the fundamental or first mode of vibration.

(e) F is the ratio defined by equation 1 and W is the ratio defined by equation 2.

Equation 1: $F = \dfrac{\text{Frequency of first mode of vibration}}{\text{Frequency of mode of vibration shown}}$

Equation 2: $W = \dfrac{\text{Wavelength of mode of vibration shown}}{\text{Wavelength of first mode of vibration}}$

(i) State the value of F.
(ii) State the value of W.
(CCEA June 2009)

2. In a normal six string guitar the top string is tuned so that its lowest natural frequency is 82 Hz when the full length of the string vibrates. The diagram opposite represents the guitar but only the top string has been shown.

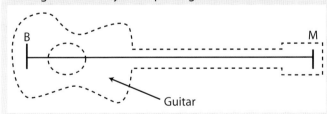

(a)(i) Copy the diagram and draw the first mode of vibration (fundamental) for the string.
(ii) Label every node with an N and every antinode with an A.

(b) (i) If the distance between B and M is 0.84 m, what is the wavelength of the first mode of vibration of the standing wave on the string?

(ii) To produce a note of higher frequency the guitarist places one finger at a point X on the string. The string cannot move at that point and the vibrating length is effectively reduced. He then plucks the string with another finger between X and B. The note obtained has a fundamental frequency of 328 Hz. Calculate the distance X to B.

(c) Guitarists are able to produce different modes of vibration on the same length of string by lightly touching the string. This creates a node at the point touched but does not reduce the effective length of the string that is vibrating.

Copy the diagram below and sketch the simplest mode of vibration that results when a guitarist touches the string at position F. The distance FM is 0.28 m and the distance BM is 0.84 m.

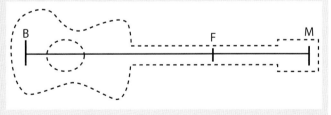

(CCEA June 2011)

Standing Waves in Air Columns

When the apparatus is set up as shown on the next page, sound waves from the speaker or tuning fork meet the reflected waves from the bottom of the air column and a standing wave is created. When a standing wave is produced the sound becomes much louder. Upon removing the glass tube there should be a very noticeable decrease in the loudness of the sound. The different frequencies at which this happens are called overtones. The lowest frequency of sound which creates a standing wave for a particular length of air column is called the fundamental.

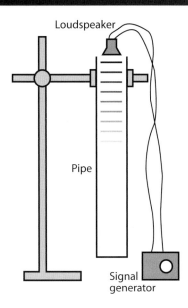

The ratio of the overtones compared with the fundamental are f_0, $3f_0$, $5f_0$, $7f_0$ etc, ie odd numbers.

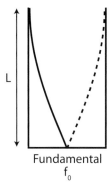 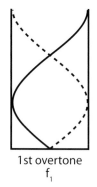 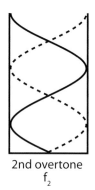 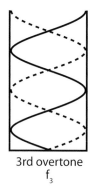

| Fundamental f_0 | 1st overtone f_1 | 2nd overtone f_2 | 3rd overtone f_3 |

Fundamental frequency = f_0 and $\lambda_0 = 4L$
Using the wave equation $v = f\lambda$ gives $\quad f_0 = \dfrac{v}{4L}$

First overtone frequency = f_1 and $\lambda_1 = \dfrac{4L}{3}$
Using $v = f\lambda$ gives $\quad f_1 = \dfrac{3v}{4L}$

Second overtone frequency = f_2 and $\lambda_2 = \dfrac{4L}{5}$
Using $v = f\lambda$ gives $\quad f_2 = \dfrac{5v}{4L}$

Fixed Frequency – Varying Length of Air Column

As the length of the air column is gradually increased, the loudness of the sound noticeably increases (resonates) at certain lengths. At each of these lengths a standing wave is created. The shortest length is known as the 1st position of resonance and corresponds to the fundamental frequency. The next two lengths at which a standing wave is created are known as the 2nd and 3rd positions of resonance.

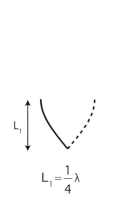 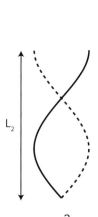 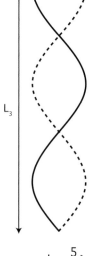

$$L_1 = \frac{1}{4}\lambda \qquad L_2 = \frac{3}{4}\lambda \qquad L_3 = \frac{5}{4}\lambda$$

Students should be able to:

2.5.1 describe and explain simple diffraction phenomena; and

2.5.2 state qualitatively, and draw diagrams to illustrate, the effect of aperture size on diffraction;

Diffraction

As waves go through a gap they spread out. This is called **diffraction**. Diffraction increases as the size of the gap is gradually decreased. The greatest diffraction happens when the size of the gap is about the same as the wavelength of the wave. The wavelength of the wave does not change as a result of diffraction.

Diffraction of sound takes place at an open door because the wavelength of sound is similar in size to the width of the door. Light has a much smaller wavelength so very narrow openings or slits are required to observe diffraction of light. A laser beam can be directed through a slit and onto a screen as shown below.

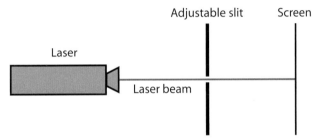

Diffraction of the light waves at a single slit produces a diffraction pattern like that shown below. As the light waves spread out in some directions destructive interference occurs, producing the dark bands. In other directions constructive interference occurs, producing the bright bands.

For the same slit width, red light has a wider diffraction pattern than blue light. The wavelength of red is greater than the wavelength of blue. As the width of the slit decreases the width of the diffraction pattern increases.

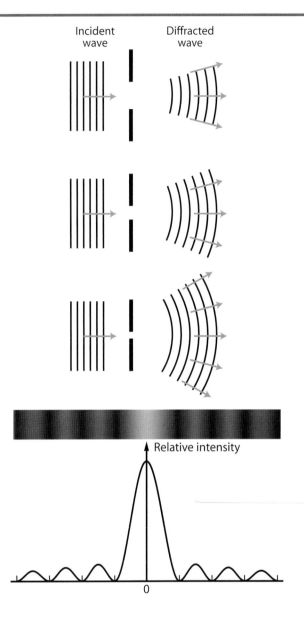

Exercise 24

1. (a) Explain what is meant by diffraction.

   (b) The diagram below is a scale diagram showing parallel wavefronts approaching an aperture. Copy and complete the diagram by carefully drawing four wavefronts after they have passed through the aperture.

   (c) In terms of diffraction, explain why people can hear a conversation through an open door even when they cannot see the people talking.
   (CCEA June 2009)

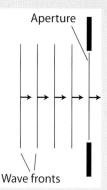

2. Residents of a housing development near a busy motorway are shielded from the noise by a barrier. The diagram below is a plan view of the situation showing houses (A to J), sound wavefronts from the motorway and the barrier.

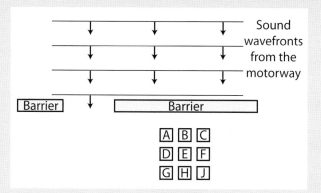

   (a) On the diagram continue the path of the sound wavefront, as it passes the barrier, to show it in its next three positions.
   (b) State and explain what will happen to the shadow zone (the region behind the noise barrier into which no sound enters) when the mean wavelength of the sound from the motorway increases.
   (CCEA June 2011)

2.6 Sound

Students should be able to:

2.6.1 determine the frequency of a pure note using a cathode ray oscilloscope;

2.6.2 perform and describe an experiment to measure the speed of sound in air using a resonance tube (end correction is not required);

2.6.3 use the formula Intensity level/dB $= 10 \lg_{10} \dfrac{I}{I_0}$

2.6.4 interpret, qualitatively, graphs of frequency and intensity response for the ear;

Sound Waves

Sound is a longitudinal wave. As sound travels through the air, the air molecules are made to vibrate parallel to the direction of propagation of the sound. This means that the molecules are in places closer together than they would normally be and in other places they are further apart than normal.

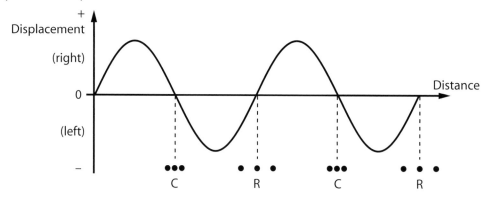

Sound travels through the air as a series of compressions and rarefactions – it is in effect a pressure wave. A sound wave is normally represented as a displacement versus distance graph.

Measuring the Frequency of Sound

A sound wave, when it reaches a microphone, produces an electrical signal which can be displayed on a cathode ray oscilloscope (CRO). A CRO display is a graph of voltage (y axis) against time (x axis). In this case, the frequency of the electrical signal is the same as that of the sound wave.

Worked Example

The diagram shows the trace obtained on a CRO when a particular sound is detected by the microphone. The time base setting in this case was 2 ms/cm. What is the frequency of the sound waves?

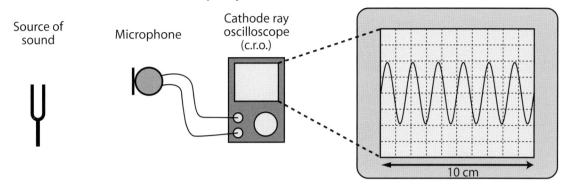

The screen displays 6 complete waves.
The x axis is 10 cm long so the total time displayed is $10 \times 2 = 20$ ms.
The period T of 1 wave $= 20 \div 6 = 3.33$ ms $= 0.0033$ s
Frequency $= 1 \div T = 1 \div 0.0033 = 333$ Hz

Measuring the Speed of Sound in Air

Standing waves of sound in air provide a method of measuring the speed of sound in air. This is one of the experiments prescribed by the CCEA Specification for AS 2.

Method 1 – Using the Fundamental Mode

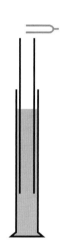

In this approach tuning forks of known frequencies are used to create standing waves. The tuning fork is made to vibrate and then held over the open end of a glass tube. The glass tube is raised or lowered until the fundamental mode of vibration is produced. This is the shortest length of the air column at which the sound becomes noticeably louder. The length of the air column is measured.

This procedure is repeated for a number of tuning forks of different frequencies. In the fundamental mode of vibration the length of the air column L is ¼ of the wavelength of the sound.

Using this fact in the wave equation gives
$v = f\lambda$ and $\lambda = 4L$ so $v = 4Lf$
The variables are L and f re-arranging gives
$$L = \frac{v}{4f}$$
The equation of a straight line passing through the origin is $y = mx$.

Hence a graph of L (y axis) against $\frac{1}{f}$ (x axis) yields a straight line.

The gradient of this line equals $\frac{v}{4}$.

An example of the results and graph from such an experiment is shown below.

Frequency of the tuning fork f/Hz	Length of the Air column L/m	$\frac{1}{f}$ /Hz⁻¹
512	0.165	1.95×10^{-3}
480	0.180	2.08×10^{-3}
362	0.235	2.76×10^{-3}
304	0.280	3.29×10^{-3}
256	0.335	3.91×10^{-3}

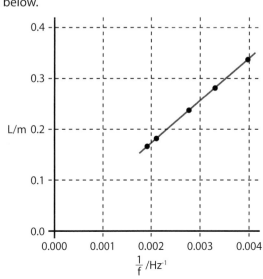

Method 2 – Using the 1st and 2nd Positions of Resonance

In this method one frequency is used. The fundamental mode of vibration is first found.

This is the shortest length of the air column at which a loud sound is heard. The length L_1 of the air column is measured. Using the same frequency the length of the air column is increased until the next mode of vibration is found. The length L_2 of the air column is then measured.

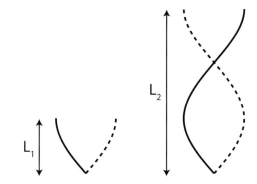

$$L_1 = \frac{\lambda}{4} \quad \text{and} \quad L_2 = \frac{3\lambda}{4} \quad \text{therefore} \quad L_2 - L_1 = \frac{\lambda}{2}$$

If we double this we can write $\lambda = 2(L_2 - L_1)$

Using the wave equation $v = f\lambda$ we can now calculate the velocity v since we know both the frequency f and the wavelength λ. This method should be repeated for a number of frequencies and an average value for the velocity of sound calculated.

Worked Example

*A signal generator is connected to a loudspeaker and a cathode ray oscilloscope (CRO). The diagram below represents the display on the oscilloscope. The grid on the oscilloscope screen is divided into centimetres. If the time base control of the oscilloscope is set to **40 μs cm⁻¹**, determine the frequency of the sound wave.*

(CCEA June 2011)

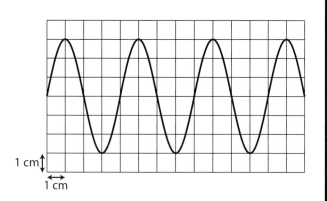

The display shows 3 ½ waves.
The width of the display is 14 cm.
Using the timebase setting this represents $14 \times 40 = 560$ μs.
The period of 1 wave is $560 \div 3.5 = 160$ μs.
Frequency = 1 ÷ period.
    Remember to convert μs (microseconds) to seconds.
Frequency = $1 \div 160 \times 10^{-6} = 6250$ Hz

Worked Example

The diagram shows a pipe of length 0.88 m, closed at one end, in air.

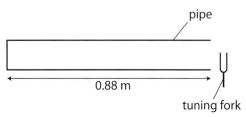

Resonance is obtained when a vibrating tuning fork of frequency 288 Hz is held over the open end. The air in the pipe is then in its second mode of oscillation.
(a) Copy the diagram and illustrate the second mode of oscillation. Mark the positions of all nodes and antinodes. Use the letter N for each node and the letter A for each antinode.

(b) Calculate the speed of sound in air.

(a)

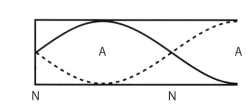

(b) In this mode of vibration the length of the air column is ¾ the wavelength of the sound.
The wavelength $\lambda = (4 \times 0.88) \div 3 = 1.17$ m.
The speed is found from the wave equation:
$v = f\lambda = 288 \times 1.17 = 337$ ms⁻¹.

Exercise 25

1. The diagram shows the trace displayed on the screen of a cathode ray oscilloscope due to the sound of a pure note. The larger squares on the grid are one cm squares.

   The time base setting of the cathode ray oscilloscope is 2.00 ms cm⁻¹. Calculate the frequency of the pure note.
   (CCEA June 2010)

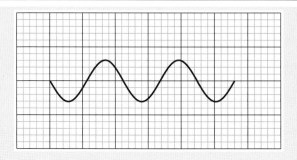

2. A resonance tube and a number of tuning forks of different frequency are used to determine the velocity of sound in air by locating the first resonance position for each tuning fork. For the first or fundamental position of the resonance the length of the air column in the tube is L. The diagram shows a typical arrangement.

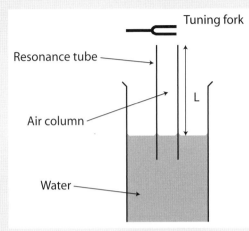

Tuning fork

Resonance tube →

L

Air column

Water →

(a) Copy the diagram and mark on it the position of the node (N) and the antinode (A) in the air column.
(b) How would an experimenter know that resonance has occurred?
(c) (i) State the relationship between the resonant length L and the wavelength λ of the sound.
(ii) Hence show that $\frac{1}{f} = \frac{4L}{v}$, where v is the velocity of sound.
(CCEA June 2008)

3. An experiment is conducted to measure the speed of sound in air using a resonance tube and tuning forks. The frequency of each tuning fork is recorded and the corresponding tube length at the first position of resonance is measured. The data recorded is shown in the table below.

Frequency / Hz	256	288	320	456	512
Tube length / m	0.312	0.277	0.258	0.189	0.166
$(\frac{1}{\text{tube length}})$ / m^{-1}					

(a) Copy and complete the table above by calculating the values of $\frac{1}{\text{tube length}}$.

(b) Plot a graph of frequency (y-axis) against $\frac{1}{\text{tube length}}$ (x-axis). Draw the line of best fit through the plotted points.
(c) Measure the gradient of the graph and state its unit.
(d) Use the gradient to calculate the speed of sound in air.
(CCEA June 2009)

4. The diagram shows a loudspeaker mounted near the open end of a tube of length 1.40 m. The loudspeaker is connected to a variable frequency a.c. supply. The frequency of the supply is gradually increased. The sound heard becomes very loud at several distinct frequencies.

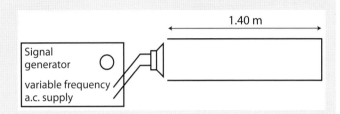

1.40 m

Signal generator
variable frequency a.c. supply

(a) (i) Describe how the standing waves that cause the loud sounds are formed.
(ii) One such loud sound is heard when the frequency is 304 Hz.
The speed of sound in air is 340 ms^{-1}.
Calculate the wavelength of the sound wave.
(iii) Copy the diagram and sketch the standing wave formed in the tube at a frequency of 304 Hz.

(b) The air in the tube is replaced with helium gas, in which the speed of sound is 965 ms^{-1}. Calculate the minimum frequency of sound that would be required to produce a standing wave in the same tube.
(CCEA January 2011)

Sound Intensity – Intensity Level – Decibel Scale

The **intensity** of sound is measured in joules per second per square metre, ie Wm^{-2}. The lowest intensity of sound that the human ear can detect is called the threshold of hearing and is 10^{-12} W m^{-2}. Loudness is a subjective quantity, it varies from person to person, it is related to sound intensity. **Intensity level** takes into account the logarithmic response of the ear. Intensity levels are measured in decibels (dB):

Intensity level in dB $= 10 \lg_{10} \frac{I}{I_0}$

Frequency and Intensity Response of the Human Ear

The range of human hearing is from **20 Hz to 20 kHz**. The graph on the next page shows the intensity of the threshold of hearing at different frequencies. The threshold of hearing has its lowest intensity value at around 2000 Hz. The value is 1.0 × 10^{-12} Wm^{-2}. The intensity level corresponding to this threshold of hearing is 0 dB.

At low frequencies the ear is very insensitive. The intensity of the threshold of hearing at 20 Hz is about 1 Wm^{-2}, a very loud sound. As the frequency increases, the **threshold of hearing** decreases, reaching a minimum at around 2 kHz. It then rises again.

Any sound with a frequency and an intensity or intensity level value that lies inside the shaded area will be heard. Any sound with a frequency and intensity or intensity level value falling in the white area will not be heard. The width of the curve will give the range of frequencies that can be heard for a particular intensity or intensity level value.

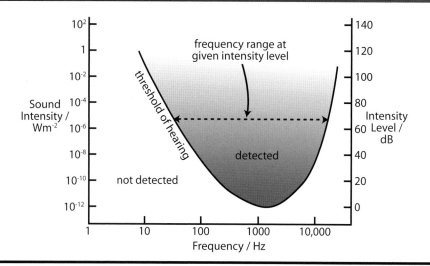

Worked Example

At point X, 20 m from a loudspeaker the intensity of the sound is 9.9×10^{-5} W m^{-2}.
(a) Calculate the sound intensity level at X.
(b) Sound from the loudspeaker is now amplified. This increases the sound intensity level at X by 6.0 dB from the value obtained in (a).
(i) Calculate the new sound intensity level at X.
(ii) Calculate the corresponding factor by which the sound intensity at X is increased.
(CCEA January 2010)

(a) $\text{intensity level} = 10 \lg\left(\dfrac{I}{I_0}\right) = 10 \lg\left(\dfrac{9.9 \times 10^{-5}}{1.0 \times 10^{-12}}\right) = 10 \lg(9.9 \times 10^{7}) = 79.96 \, \text{dB}$ or 80 dB to nearest dB

(b) (i) New intensity level = 80 + 6.0 = 86 dB

    (ii) $86 = 10 \lg\left(\dfrac{I_{new}}{I_0}\right)$ Thus $8.6 = \lg\left(\dfrac{I_{new}}{1.0 \times 10^{-12}}\right)$

    $I_{new} = 10^{8.6} \times 1.0 \times 10^{-12} = 4 \times 10^{8} \times 1.0 \times 10^{-12} = 4 \times 10^{-4} \, \text{Wm}^{-2}$

    $\text{Factor} = I_{new} \div I = 4 \times 10^{-4} \div 9.9 \times 10^{-5} = 4$

Exercise 26

1. The graph shows the intensity response with frequency of a human ear. It is used as a measure of perceived loudness which matches the response of the human ear.

(a) State the main feature of the scale which allows it to match the response of the ear.
(b) Dogs have a range of hearing from approximately 20 Hz to 50 kHz.
(i) State one similarity and one difference between the frequency range of a dog and a human.
(ii) Using the intensity level/dB scale for a human ear, the intensity level corresponding to the threshold of hearing of a dog is −20dB. Dogs' ears are most sensitive at a frequency of 5000 Hz. Copy the graph and on it sketch a graph of the intensity response with frequency of a dog's ear. The curve should have a similar shape to that of the human ear.

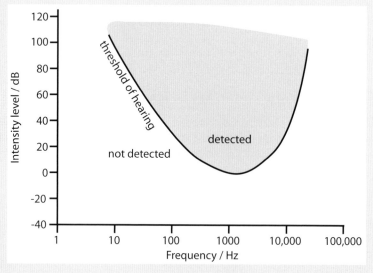

(iii) Describe and explain the difference in how a sound of frequency 5000 Hz would be perceived by a human and a dog.
(CCEA January 2011)

2.7 Imaging Techniques

Students should be able to:

2.7.1 describe the flexible endoscope in terms of structure, technique and applications;

2.7.2 describe ultrasonic A-scans and B-scans in terms of physical principles, basic equipment, technique and applications;

2.7.3 describe CT scans in terms of physical principles, basic equipment, technique and applications;

2.7.4 describe MRI scans in terms of physical principles, basic equipment, technique and applications;

Endoscopy

An endoscope is a flexible tube that allows us to look into the body. In many cases there is no need to perform surgery to do this. In other cases, a small incision is required to perform what has become known as key-hole surgery. The development of optical fibre in the 1960s allow the construction of endoscopes that were both flexible and of small diameter. When light travels from glass into air it is refracted away from the normal. However if the angle of incidence in the glass exceeds the critical angle then total internal reflection takes place. This allows light to travel along a glass tube as shown. If the glass tube is flexible, and the angles through which the glass fibre is bent are not too great, the light can be directed into body cavities.

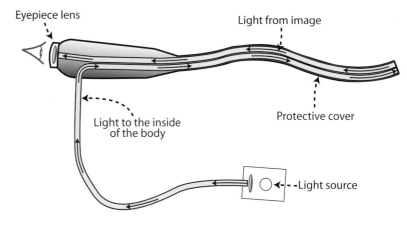

The endoscope has two bundles of optical fibres. One is called the **illumination bundle** and carries light to the object being viewed. The other bundle, the **image bundle**, carries back the reflected light. The optical fibres inside the image bundle are carefully arranged parallel to each other to create what is termed a **coherent** bundle.

Ultrasound

Typical diagnostic ultrasound frequencies used in medicine are in the range 1 MHz to 15 MHz. Low intensity ultrasonic waves pass through tissue without causing harm, unlike X rays which cause ionisation and damage cells. Ultrasonic waves are reflected at the boundaries between biological structures. These reflections allow images of internal organs to be created by an ultrasound scanner.

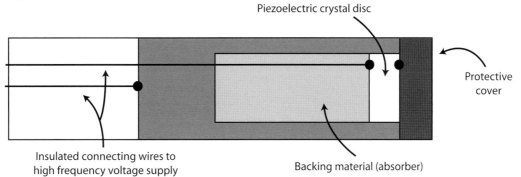

The ultrasound transducer probe generates and receives sound waves using a principle called the **piezoelectric effect**. When a high frequency alternating voltage is applied to certain crystals, the crystals vibrate at the same frequency as the applied alternating voltage.

The backing material is used to prevent the crystal oscillations continuing when the alternating voltage is removed. This ensures the pulse ends abruptly. A silver electrode attached to the piezoelectric crystal provides the electrical connection to the high frequency voltage supply.

The ultrasound waves are emitted in short pulses that may last for only 5μs. There is then gap of 100 μs.

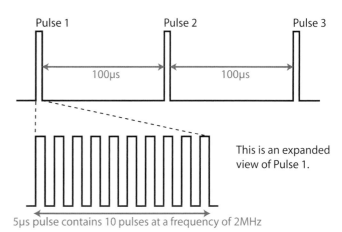

This is an expanded view of Pulse 1.

5μs pulse contains 10 pulses at a frequency of 2MHz

During the 100 μs the transducer is in receive mode – it receives reflected waves. These reflected waves cause changes in the shape of the piezoelectric crystal which produces an electrical voltage which is detected and processed by a computer system.

A Scan

The A in 'A scan' means **amplitude**. When used in this way, a pulse of ultrasound is sent into the body and its reflection is displayed in the manner shown below. The horizontal axis on the display represents time and the vertical axis represents the amplitude of the reflected wave.

In the diagram, an ultrasound scanner is used to scan a foetus. The ultrasound waves are reflected from various structures within the womb and this method is commonly used to measure the diameter of the foetal head.

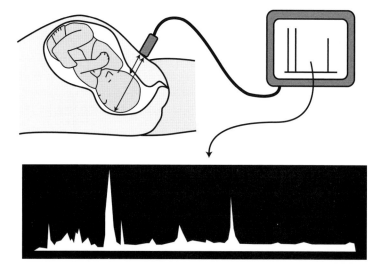

B Scan

The B in 'B scan' means brightness. The B scan produces an image that is easier to interpret. The ultrasound probe is scanned across the body in a series of lines. The strength and position of the reflected ultrasound is stored electronically. The data stored is then used to produce an image on a TV screen. The strength of the signal is used to determine the brightness of the spot on the screen. B scans can identify tumours in the liver and other organs. The most common use is to monitor foetal development.

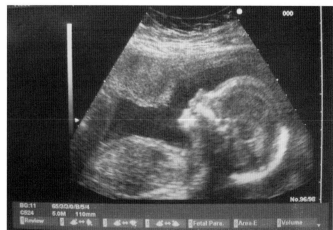

Computed Tomography or CT Scanning

Computed Tomography (CT) imaging, also known as **CAT scanning** (Computed Axial Tomography), has the unique ability to image a combination of soft tissue, bone, and blood vessels. A **tomograph** is a detailed image of the structure of an object (body) through one plane. CT uses a digital computer together with a rotating X-ray device (as shown in the diagram on the right) to create detailed tomographs (cross sectional images or 'slices') of the different organs and body parts such as the lungs, liver, kidneys, brain, spine, and blood vessels.

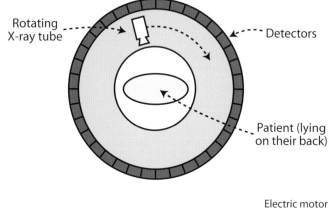

How are X-rays Produced?

X-rays are produced by high speed electrons striking metal targets. The electrons are emitted by a **cathode** which is heated to a very high temperature (white heat). This heating is produced by an electric current passing through the cathode. The electrons are then accelerated toward a metal **anode** using a very high voltage (typically 100 kV).

At the centre of the anode is a metal target. This target is made of metal of a high melting point and high atomic number. Around **0.5%** of the electrons produce **X-rays**, the other 99.5% simply heat the anode. The anode therefore needs to be constantly cooled. In the case of the rotating anode tube shown above this is achieved by conduction, convection and radiation.

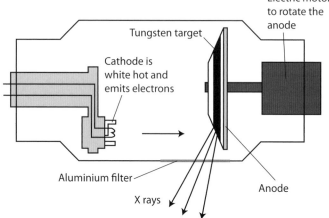

The diagram below shows a typical X ray spectrum. There are three characteristics that must be understood.

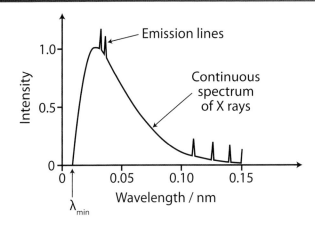

1. The Continuous Spectrum

When the high speed electrons encounter the atoms of the target material they are slowed by the attraction of the positively charged nucleus. The energy lost by the electron appears as an X-ray photon. The electrons lose varying amounts of energy so X-rays photons of different energy (wavelength, frequency) are produced. This type of X-ray production is known as **braking radiation** as shown in the diagram.

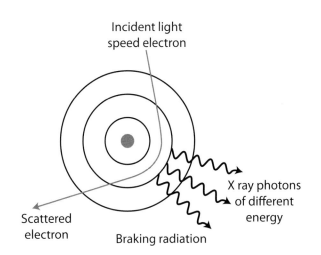

2. The Minimum Wavelength λ_{min}

Some high speed electrons lose all of their kinetic energy in a single encounter with the atoms of the target material. This produces an X-ray photon with maximum energy (minimum wavelength or maximum frequency). The value of λ_{min} can be calculated.

The kinetic energy of the electron = loss of electric potential energy = eV

where   e is charge of the electron
        V is the tube voltage.

The energy of this X-ray photon $= \dfrac{hc}{\lambda_{min}} = eV$.

3. The Sharp Emission Lines

These are characteristic of the element used as the target. These elements have high atomic numbers and consequently the electron shells are generally filled with the total complement of electrons. An incoming electron will knock an electron out of these filled electrons shells, as shown in the diagram. The vacancy left is immediately filled by a electron from a higher energy shell dropping down to a lower energy shell. It loses its energy as an X-ray of very specific energy or wavelength.

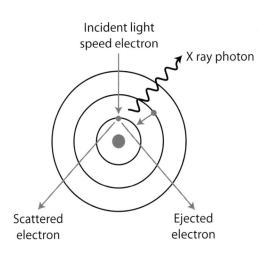

Magnetic Resonance Imaging (MRI)

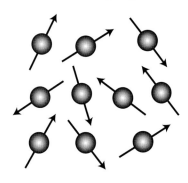

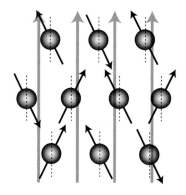

The basis for this technique is **Nuclear Magnetic Resonance** or NMR. Although it involves the nuclei of atoms the only radiation involved is that of radio signals.

The nuclei in some atomic nuclei spin and this spinning positive electric charge creates a magnetic field. You can think of the spinning nuclei as subatomic bar magnets. When no magnetic field is present the nuclei are randomly orientated but when placed in a magnetic field they line up with the magnetic field.

However, the picture is a little more complicated. Because of thermal motion, the spinning nuclei wobble about the axis of rotation, as shown in the diagram. This effect is called **precession**. The frequency at which they wobble is known as the **Larmour frequency**. If an electromagnetic radio frequency pulse is applied at this frequency, then the nuclei can absorb that energy. This results in the nuclei in the lower energy state jumping to the higher energy state and they are now aligned in a direction opposite to that of the magnetic field direction.

Some of the nuclei become aligned in the same direction as the magnetic field and some become aligned in the opposite direction to the magnetic field. This means there are two spin states for the nuclei, those nuclei that become lined up with the magnetic field are in the lower energy state. Those nuclei that have become aligned in direction opposite to the magnetic field are in the higher of the two energy states.

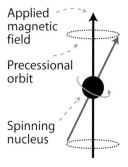

Applied magnetic field

Precessional orbit

Spinning nucleus

When the pulse of radio waves is stopped, the nuclei return to the lower energy state and as they do they re-emit the radio wave they absorbed. It is this re-emitted radio wave that is detected and processed to provide information on tissues in the body.

Similar atoms in different environments, such as a hydrogen attached to an oxygen and a hydrogen attached to a carbon, flip at different frequencies. This provides us with a means of discriminating between different soft tissues in the body. X-rays are of limited use in this respect.

The patient is placed inside the field gradient coils as shown in the diagram. There are actually three such coils, and they are used to produce changes in the steady magnetic field which allows the location of the emitted radio signals from the patient to be located. Surrounding the patient is the magnetic field produced by a super conducting magnet. The patient is placed on the table which is then slid inside the large cavity which contains the magnetic field and radio coils.

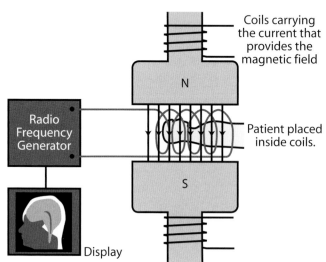

Radio Frequency Generator

Coils carrying the current that provides the magnetic field

N

Patient placed inside coils.

S

Display

A pulse of radio waves is emitted by the coils surrounding the patient. This causes the hydrogen nuclei to flip to the higher energy state.

The radio waves are then switched off and as the hydrogen nuclei return to the lower energy state they emit radio signals. These radio signals are detected and with use of computers are processed to provide a display of the tissues in the body.

Summary of Imaging Techniques

Technique	Advantages	Disadvantages	Most suited to
Endoscopy	Removes the need for major surgery. Does not expose the patient to ionising radiation.	Can be an uncomfortable experience for the patient.	It is mostly used to diagnose problems in the oesophagus, stomach and intestines. Can be used to take a small sample of tissue for analysis (biopsy). Laparascopy is an extension of the technique where the endoscope is used to look inside the abdomen and pelvis through a small incision. Endoscopic (keyhole) surgery can be used to treat hernias and remove tumours.
Ultrasound	It is thought to be safe as it doesn't use an ionising radiation.	Limited in its ability to see very fine detail.	Detecting cysts, which are pockets of fluid in the liver, ovaries and breasts. Used to identify gallstones and kidney stones. Commonly used during pregnancy to check on the development of the foetus. Useful in diagnosing blockages in blood vessels.
CT scanning	Takes a relatively short time to complete.	The radiation dose is about 100 times that of standard chest X-ray.	Useful for diagnosing internal injuries in trauma victims such as those involved in a car crash. CT scans are used to show a range of very different tissues clearly such as lung, bone, soft tissue and blood vessels.
M R I	Is based on the detection of radio waves and not ionising radiation. Requires strong magnetic field which is though to be safe. Can produce images that allow very fine detail to be seen.	The strong magnetic field requires special safety measures with regards to metal objects. A scan can takes up to 20 minutes. The changing magnetic field can be noisy and frightening to patients.	Can be used to identify tumours. Can identify multiple sclerosis. Often used on athletes to identify ligament damage and problems in the knee and other joints. Used to examine the anatomy of the brain and how it works. MRI can reveal the small differences between tissues that are very similar.

Exercise 27

1. (a) The main components of an MRI scanner are the scanner magnet, field gradient coils, rf transmitter, rf receiver and computer. Describe briefly the function of (i) the field gradient coils (ii) the computer.
   (b) Describe how the magnetic field of the scanner magnet is created. Explain how recent advances in technology have vastly reduced the cost of producing the magnetic field.
   (c) Outline three advantages of MRI compared to CT scanning.
   (CCEA January 2011)

2. Ultrasound scanning can be used in non-invasive examinations of internal structure of the human body.

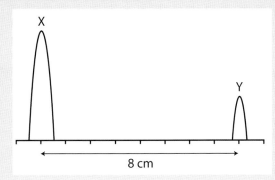

The diagram shows output from an ultrasound A scan used to measure the thickness of bone. The ultrasound pulses are converted to electrical signals and displayed on the screen of a CRO. Pulse X is the first reflected pulse and Y the second reflected pulse.

The time base of the CRO is set to 1 μs per cm.
(a) Explain why pulse X is of greater amplitude than pulse Y.
(b) If the speed of ultrasound in bone is 4000 ms⁻¹, calculate the thickness of the bone.
(CCEA January 2010)

3. Computed tomography (CT) scanning is a powerful diagnostic tool making use of X-rays.
   (a) What is a "tomograph"?
   (b) X rays are produced in two distinct ways. Both ways involve high energy electrons being fired at a tungsten target. Outline the mechanisms by which the high energy incident electrons produce X-rays once they strike the tungsten target.
   (c) The diagram on the next page shows a simplified diagram of an X-ray tube in which the tungsten target is embedded in a large mass of copper all of which rotates.

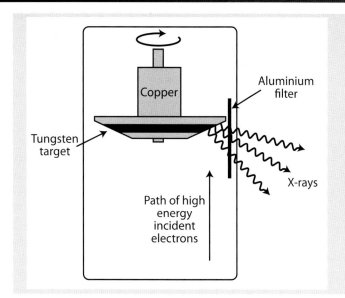

(i) Approximately 1% of the incident energy of the electrons is converted to X-rays. State what happens to the remaining 99% and explain how the structure of the X-ray tube shown has been designed to cope with 99% energy loss.
(ii) The emerging X-rays are passed through a 3 mm thick aluminium filter thereby removing the lower energy X-ray radiation. Explain why this is necessary.
(CCEA June 2011)

2.8 Photon Model

Students should be able to:

2.8.1 recall and use the formula E = hf;

2.8.2 use the photon model to explain the photoelectric effect qualitatively using the terms 'photon energy' and 'work function';

Photoelectric Emission

Electrons are ejected from the surface of a metal when electromagnetic radiation of sufficiently high frequency falls on it. This is called the **photoelectric effect**. The electrons emitted by this process are called **photoelectrons**. To explain this effect we need to use the **photon model** of light. In this model we regard light as packets or **quanta** of energy. These quanta are called **photons**.

The energy of a photon is given by:

$E = hf$ or $\dfrac{hc}{\lambda}$ where E = energy of the photon in J
h = Planck's constant = 6.63×10^{-34} Js
f = frequency of the radiation in Hz
c = speed of light = 3×10^8 ms^{-1}
λ = wavelength of the radiation in m

It is common to give the energy of a photon in electron-volts. $1eV = 1.6 \times 10^{-19}$ J.

To explain the photoelectric effect Einstein assumed that not only were light and other forms of electromagnetic radiation emitted in whole numbers of photons, but that they were also absorbed as photons.

The **work function Φ** is defined as **the minimum quantity of energy needed to liberate electrons from the surface of a metal and to just allow it to escape to an infinite distance from the metal**. Einstein proposed that a photon of energy will cause the emission of an electron from the metal if the energy of the photon is equal to or greater than the work function of the metal.

If the photon's energy is greater than the work function of the metal then the difference appears as kinetic energy of the ejected electron. Since the work function is the minimum energy needed to eject an electron from the metal this means that the electrons that are ejected will have a range of kinetic energy from zero to a maximum.

Einstein's **Photoelectric Equation** can be written as:

Incident photon – Work function = Maximum kinetic energy
energy   energy   of the electrons

or $hf - \Phi = \dfrac{1}{2}mv_{max}^2$

The frequency of the electromagnetic radiation that just liberates an electrons is called the threshold frequency f_0 and is equal to the work function F of the metal.

$hf_0 = \Phi$

Worked Example

Photons of light are incident on the surface of a photo-emissive metal.
(a) State two conditions for photoelectrons to be emitted from the metal surface.
(b) The work function of a certain metal is 3.84×10^{-19} J. It is illuminated with blue light of wavelength 450 nm. Calculate the energy of the blue photon, then state and explain if photoelectric emission will occur from this metal with this illumination.
(CCEA June 2010)

(a) 1. The energy of the incident photons must be greater than the work function of the metal.
2. The photons must be absorbed by the metal. Most of the photons are actually reflected by the metal.

(b) You need to find the energy of the incident photon as shown below.

$$E = \frac{hc}{\lambda} = \frac{6.63 \times 10^{-34} \times 3 \times 10^8}{450 \times 10^{-9}} = 4.42 \times 10^{-19} \text{ J}$$

This is greater than the work function so electrons are ejected from the metal by these blue photons.

Exercise 28

1. A polished zinc plate is illuminated with ultraviolet radiation of frequency 6.00×10^{16} Hz.

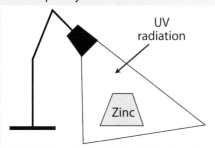

(a) What is a photon?
(b) Calculate the energy of a photon of the ultraviolet light.
(c) Explain what is meant by photoelectric emission and state the conditions under which it can occur for the zinc plate illuminated by ultraviolet radiation.
(CCEA June 2009)

2. The graph opposite illustrates the relationship between photon energy and radiation frequency.

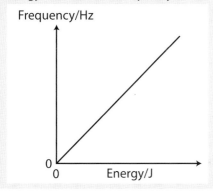

(a) What is the numerical value for the gradient of this graph.
(b) Calculate the energy of a photon if the radiation has a frequency of 200 MHz and a wavelength of 1.50 m.
(CCEA June 2011)

3. The work function of a metal is 1.85 eV
(a) Explain the meaning of the term work function.
(b) Convert the value of this work function into joules.
(c) Calculate the minimum frequency of incident radiation for photoelectrons to be emitted from this metal.
(CCEA January 2010)

4. A UV (ultraviolet) lamp is shone onto a magnesium surface.
(a)(i) Show that, for UV light of wavelength 290 nm, the energy of each photon is 6.86×10^{-19} J.
(ii) The magnesium surface has an area of 1.6×10^{-4} m². The energy delivered to each square metre every second is 0.034 J. Calculate the number of photons that fall onto the surface each second.

(b) The frequency of the UV light remains constant and the energy of the incident photons is greater than the work function of the magnesium.
(i) State and explain the effect of increasing the intensity of the radiation on the rate of emission of photoelectrons from the magnesium surface.
(ii) State and explain the effect of increasing the intensity of the radiation on the kinetic energy of the emitted photoelectrons from the magnesium surface.
(CCEA January 2011)

2.9 Quantum Physics

Students should be able to:

2.9.1 understand that electrons exist in energy levels in atoms;

2.9.2 recall and use the formula $hf = E_1 - E_2$; and

2.9.3 provide a simple explanation of laser action.

The Emission Spectrum

When sunlight is made to pass through a triangular glass prism, a spectrum is obtained (Figure 1 overleaf). We call such a spectrum continuous. We can also obtain a continuous spectrum from hot filament lamps.

However, when we look at the light from a gas discharge lamp containing a gaseous element such as sodium vapour or neon, we obtain a very limited range of wavelengths (colours) as shown in Figure 2.

Figure 1

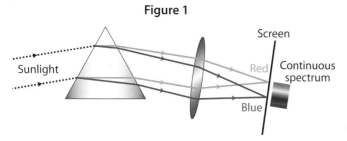

Figure 2

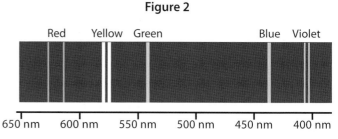

This is called a **line emission spectrum** and consists of a series of discrete wavelengths. To explain this type of emission spectrum consisting we have to apply the idea of quantisation to the electron in orbit around the nucleus of the atoms.

An electron has a fixed amount of energy in each orbit, those being closest to the nucleus having the least energy and those most distant from the nucleus having the most energy.

An electron can move from one energy level to a higher energy level by absorbing a photon of energy equal to the energy difference between the two states. This process is called **excitation**.

An electron in an excited state can move to a lower energy level, by emitting a photon of light of energy exactly equal to the energy difference between the two states would be emitted. This process is called **relaxation**.

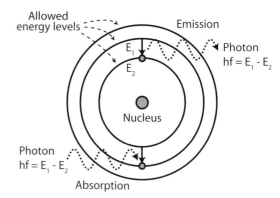

For both excitation (absorption of a photon) and relaxation (emission of a photon) the same equation applies:

$\Delta E = hf$ or $\dfrac{hc}{\lambda}$ where ΔE = energy difference between the two levels in J
$\quad h$ = Planck's constant = 6.63×10^{-34} Js
$\quad f$ = frequency of the radiation in Hz
$\quad c$ = speed of light = 3×10^8 ms^{-1}
$\quad \lambda$ = wavelength of the radiation in m.

You should appreciate that the equation above is an example of the principle of conservation of energy in a form that applies to electron transitions between orbits.

Energy Level Diagrams

An **energy level diagram** is shown below. It shows the main electron transitions in hydrogen. The lowest energy level or ground state has value of –13.6 eV.
Higher energy levels are less negative, –3.4 eV, –1.5 eV and so on.
The energy levels are often given in electron–volts.
1 eV = 1.6×10^{-19} J.

The energy levels are negative since energy has to be supplied to remove the electron completely from the atom.

The **longest wavelength** in this series corresponds to a photon with minimum energy. This photon is emitted when the electron moves from level with energy –3.4 eV to the ground state level with energy –13.6 eV.

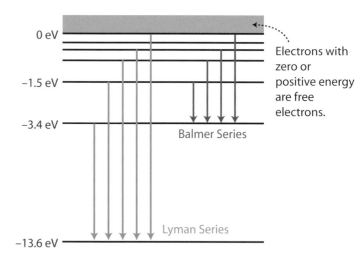

The energy of the emitted photon = 13.6 – 3.4 = 10.2 eV = 1.63×10^{-18} J. The frequency f = $\Delta E \div h$ giving a value of 2.46×10^{15} Hz and a wavelength of 121.9 nm.

The **shortest wavelength** in this series corresponds to a photon with maximum energy. This photon is emitted when the electron moves from an energy of 0 to the ground state level of energy –13.6 eV.

The energy of the emitted photon = 13.6 – 0 = 13.6 eV = 2.18×10^{-18} J. The frequency f = $\Delta E \div h$ giving a value of 3.29×10^{15} Hz and a wavelength of 91.2 nm.

Remember 1 nm (nano–metre) = 1×10^{-9} m

Worked Example

The electron in a particular hydrogen atom is in the ground state. It can be excited to a higher energy level by absorbing energy from incident radiation of suitable wavelength.

(a) (i) What is an energy level?
  (ii) Explain what is meant by "in the ground state".
(b) The diagram shows the lowest two energy levels for the hydrogen atom.

————————————————— –3.34 eV

————————————————— –13.6 eV

  (i) Explain why the energy levels are negative.
  (ii) Calculate the wavelength of the incident radiation which will excite the electron in the ground state to the next energy level.

(c) Explain why hydrogen does absorb visible light when its electron is in the ground state.
(CCEA January 2010)

(a) (i) An energy level corresponds to allowed electron orbit were the electron has a fixed amount of energy.
   (ii) This is the lowest energy level that the orbiting electron can have and corresponds to an orbit closest to the nucleus.

(b) (i) Electrons that are free, i.e. not bound to a nucleus, can have any energy from zero to any positive value. To free an electron from an atom requires energy to be given to the electron so by convention we allocate a negative value to electron energy levels in the atom.
   (ii) $E = E_1 - E_2 = (-3.34) - (-13.6) \times 1.6 \times 10^{-19} = 1.64 \times 10^{18}$ J

(c) The energy of a photon of visible light does equal the energy level difference between the ground state and the next excited energy level so it cannot be absorbed.

Exercise 29

1. Energy levels in atoms are described as being quantised.
   (a) State the meaning of the term quantised.
   (b) When electromagnetic radiation passes through hydrogen, some frequencies of radiation are absorbed. The graph shows how the intensity of light transmitted through a sample of hydrogen depends on the frequency of the light.

   (i) Calculate the energy of the photons associated with the maximum absorption shown.
   (ii) The table lists the 4 lowest energy levels of the hydrogen atom.

–0.85 eV
–1.50 eV
–3.39 eV
–13.6 eV

   Between which levels does the does the electron transition occur if the electron absorbs a photon of energy calculated in part (i)? State clearly the direction of the transition.
   (CCEA January 2011)

2. The diagram opposite illustrates the electron energy levels, with their values of energy, in a hypothetical atom.

   For each of the following scenarios, state what will happen, or what must have happened, and explain your answer in terms of the conservation of energy principle.
   (a) An electron at n = 2 interacts with a quantum of energy equal to 300 eV.
   (b) An electron at n = 3 is struck by a photon of energy 5.7 eV.
   (c) A photon of frequency 3.94×10^{16} Hz is emitted.
   (CCEA June 2011)

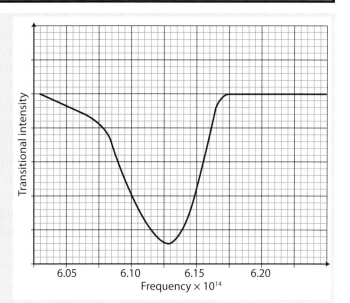

Level	Energy
$n = \infty$	0 eV
$n = 4$	–0.4 eV
$n = 3$	–6.0 eV
$n = 2$	–54.4 eV
$n = 1$	–217.7 eV

Laser Action

The length of time an electron spends in an excited state is typically 10^{-8} s. It then makes a transition to a lower energy level and a photon of light is emitted. This process is called **spontaneous emission**.

Some excited energy levels allow the electrons to spend a longer time in them. These are called metastable levels and the time spent can be around 10^{-3} s. This gives time to have more electrons in this excited state than in the ground state. This is called a **population inversion**.

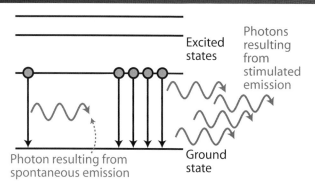

A photon resulting from spontaneous emission can induce many of the electrons in a metastable excited state to make simultaneous transitions to the lower energy level so producing a lot of photons at the same time. This means that the light emitted by a laser is coherent. This is known as **stimulated emission**.

Exercise 30

1. The diagram illustrates the electron arrangement within the atoms of a laser before it can be switched on. Most of the electrons are in their ground state with an occasional electron in an excited state.

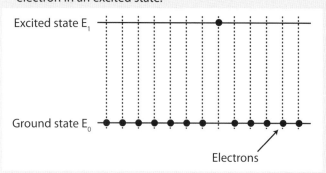

(a) (i) Copy the diagram and draw a possible electron arrangement when the laser is switched on.
(ii) What name is given to this situation?
(iii) Spontaneous emission occurs when an electron randomly falls to the ground state. What causes the electron to fall due to stimulated emission?
(CCEA June 2009)

2.10 Wave – Particle Duality

Students should be able to:

2.10.1 categorise electromagnetic wave phenomena as being explained by the wave model, the photon model or both;

2.10.2 describe electron diffraction; and

2.10.3 use the de Broglie formula $\lambda = \dfrac{h}{p}$.

Wave – Particle Duality

To explain some aspects of light behaviour, such as interference and diffraction, it is treated as a wave. To explain other aspects it is treated as being made up of particles (photons). Light exhibits **wave–particle duality**, because it exhibits properties of both waves and particles:

Phenomenon	Can be explained in terms of waves	Can be explained in terms of photons
Interference of light	Yes	No
Diffraction of light	Yes	No
Polarisation of light	Yes	No
Photoelectric effect	No	Yes

Electron Diffraction

In 1924, Louis de Broglie (pronounced de Broy), suggested that matter might also have a dual nature. He suggested that a moving particle has an associated wavelength given by the equation:

$$\lambda = \frac{h}{p}$$

where λ = de broglie wavelength (m)
h = Planck's constant (6.63×10^{-34} Js)
p = momentum of the particle (kg ms^{-1})

Calculations show that if electrons were accelerated through 100 V then their momentum would indicate a wavelength of around 10^{-10} m. This is the distance between atoms and so it might be possible to use the layers of atoms in a crystal to produce diffraction and interference effects.

This can be demonstrated using the apparatus shown. This shows how a crystal of graphite can be used to produce interference of electrons in a beam.

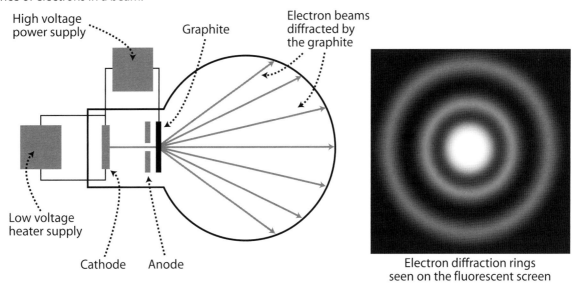

Electron diffraction rings
seen on the fluorescent screen

Where lots of electrons reach the fluorescent screen a bright ring is seen. This is a region of constructive interference. The absence of light from the screen indicates a region of destructive interference where few electrons reach the screen.

Exercise 31

1. The de Broglie formula is $\lambda = \dfrac{h}{p}$

   (a) What does each term in the formula represent?
   (b) The graph below is one of 1/p against λ.
   State the numerical value of the gradient and state its unit.

   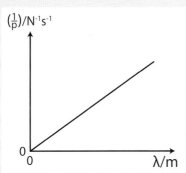

   (CCEA June 2009)

2. Some phenomena associated with electromagnetic radiation may be described using a wave model, other phenomena require a particle model for their description. For some phenomena both models are acceptable.
   (a) (i) Which model may be used to describe polarisation and the photoelectric effect?
   (ii) Name a phenomenon that can be described by either model.
   (b) Calculate the de Broglie wavelength of an alpha particle of mass 6.64×10^{-27} kg and charge 3.20×10^{-19} C ejected from a nucleus at 4.50×10^6 ms^{-1}.
   (CCEA June 2011)

3. Electron diffraction shows that electrons behave as waves.
   (a) Describe how this can be demonstrated experimentally. You may draw a diagram to aid your description.
   (b) Describe and explain the effect on the electron diffraction pattern if the incident electrons have a smaller velocity.
   (CCEA January 2010)

Answers

Exercise 1 – *Unit 1.1*

1. Pascal: $kg\ m^{-1}\ s^{-2}$; Coulomb: A s; Watt: $kg\ m^2\ s^{-3}$, Volt: $kg\ m^2\ s^{-3}\ A^{-1}$, Ohm: $kg\ m^2\ s^{-3}\ A^{-2}$.

2. Length, Mole, Temperature

3. h is measured in $kg\ m^2\ s^{-1}$

Exercise 2 – *Unit 1.2*

1. (i) Force and Acceleration only are vectors (ii) See text

2. (i) Horizontal component = 12 cos 35° = 9.82 ≈ 9.8 N
   Vertical component = 6.88 ≈ 6.9 N

   (ii) Resultant vertical force = mg – 6.9 = 3 × 9.81 – 6.9
   = 22.5 N

3.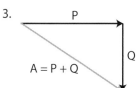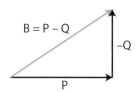

4. (i) 210 sin 55° = 172 N

   (ii) Horizontal components are equal in magnitude, but opposite in direction

   (iii) 128 cos 20° = 120 N and 210 cos 55° = 120 N

Exercise 3 – *Unit 1.3*

1. (i) 270 kmh^{-1} = 270 000 metres in 3 600 seconds
   = 270 000 m ÷ 3 600 s = 75 ms^{-1}

   (ii) a = (v - u) ÷ t = (75 – 0) / 28 = 2.68 ms^{-2}
   S = ½ (u + v)t = ½(0 + 75) × 28 = 1050 m

2. In last 60.0 metres, constant speed = distance / time =
   60.0 / 4.62 = 12.99 ms^{-1}
   In first 40 metres, S = ½ (u + v)t

   $$40 = ½(0 + 12.99)t$$
   $$t = 80 ÷ 12.99 = 6.16\ s$$

   Total time = 6.16 + 4.62 = 10.8 s (to 3 significant figures)

3. From t = 0 to t = t_1: non-uniform, decreasing acceleration from zero velocity to a uniform velocity.
   From t = t_1: to t = t_2: uniform velocity.
   From t = t_2: to t = t_3: uniform deceleration to zero velocity.

4.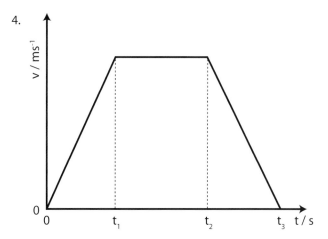

Exercise 4 – *Unit 1.3*

1. (a) speed = 0, acceleration = –9.81 ms^{-2}
   (b) $v^2 = u^2 + 2aS$. So $0^2 = 39.24^2 + 2 × (–9.81) × S$ which gives S = 78.48 m
   (c) v = u + at. so, 0 = 39.24 + (–9.81)t which gives t = 4 s

2. (a) v = u + at = 0 + (–9.81) × 5 = –49.1 ms^{-1} where the minus sign shows direction (b) average speed = ½ (u + v) = 24.6 ms^{-1}
   (c) S = average speed x time = 24.6 × 5 = 123 m

3. (a) $v^2 = u^2 + 2aS$. so $0^2 = 12^2 + 2 × (–9.81) × S$
   which gives S = 7.34 m and hence a total height of 30 + 7.34 ≈ 37.3 m
   (b) v = u + at so, 0 = 12 – 9.81 × t giving t = 1.22 s
   (c) $S = ut + ½at^2$ so, $–37.3 = 0 + ½ × (–9.81) × t^2$ which gives t = 2.76 s
   (d) v = u + at = 0 + (–9.81) × 2.76 = 27.1 ms^{-1}

4. (a) velocity = +4.00 ms^{-1}, acceleration = –9.81 ms^{-2}
   (b) $v^2 = u^2 + 2aS$. so $0^2 = 4^2 + 2 × (–9.81) × S$
   so, S = 0.8 m and hence total height = 22 + 0.8 = 22.8 m
   (c) $v^2 = u^2 + 2aS = 0^2 + 2 × (–9.81) × 22.8 = 447.3$
   giving v = –21.2 ms^{-1}
   (d) Time to reach max height: t = 4 ÷ 9.81 = 0.41 s
   Time to fall from max height to ground
   = 21.2 ÷ 9.81 = 2.16 s
   So total time = 0.41 + 2.16 = 2.57 s

Exercise 5 – *Unit 1.4*

1. (a) Horizontal velocity component = 25 ÷ 1.4 = 17.9 ms^{-1}
   Initial vertical velocity component v = u + at so,
   0 = u – 9.81 × 1.4
   u = 13.7 ms^{-1}

   (b)(i) By Pythagoras, $v = \sqrt{(17.9^2 + 13.7^2)} = 22.5\ ms^{-1}$
   (ii) θ = tan^{-1}(13.7 ÷ 17.9) = 37.4°
   (iii) S = ½ (u+v)t = ½ (13.7+0) × 1.4 = 9.59 m

2. (i) Initial vertical velocity = 9.3 sin 45 = 6.58 ms⁻¹

   (ii) For the vertical motion, the displacement S is –0.6 m, so, using $v^2 = u^2 + 2aS = 6.58^2 + 2(-9.81)(-0.6) = 55.07$

   $v = \sqrt{55.07} = 7.4$ ms⁻¹

   (iii) v = u + at, so –7.4 = 6.58 – 9.81t

   giving t = (6.58 + 7.4) ÷ 9.81 = 1.43 s

Exercise 6 – Unit 1.5

1. a = F÷m = –1200 ÷ 1800 = –0.667 ms⁻¹

   v = u + at, so 0 = 16.7 – 0.667t

   so, t = 16.7 ÷ 0.667 = 25.1 s

2. (a) Opposing forces = $2.3 \times 10^6 \times 0.6 = 1.38 \times 10^6$ N

   Resultant force = ma = $2.3 \times 10^6 \times 0.2 = 4.6 \times 10^5$ N

   Driving force = Resultant force + Opposing forces

   $= 1.38 \times 10^6 + 4.6 \times 10^5 = 1.84 \times 10^6$ N

   (b) Friction is reduced between wheel and track so resultant forward force decreases. So the acceleration decreases.

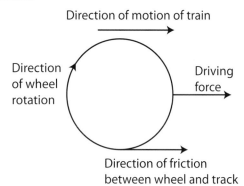

Direction of motion of train

Direction of wheel rotation

Driving force

Direction of friction between wheel and track

3. (a) See text.

   (b) (i) The brick is stationary, so by Newton's First Law the normal contact force exerted by the ground on the brick equals the weight of the brick, ie A = B.

   (ii) The downwards force exerted by the brick on the ground is equal to the normal contact force exerted by the ground on the brick, ie C = A.

   The gravitational attraction of the brick on the Earth equals the weight of the brick, ie D = B.

Exercise 7 – Unit 1.6

1. Let the distance from A to the cable C be d and **take moments about end A.**

   Sum of Anti–clockwise moments about A = Sum of Clockwise moments about A

   (Note that the weight of S₁ does not have a moment about the point A)

   430 × d + 430 × 22 = 120 × 16 + 70 × 24 + 600 × 12

   430 d + 9460 = 1920 + 1680 + 7200

   430d = 1340

   d = 3.12 m

2. Let the reaction at C be R$_C$ and the reaction at D be R$_D$.

   To find R$_C$: CWM = ACWM about point D

   R$_C$ × 100 = (0.2 × 80) + (1.2 × 50) + (0.9 × 30)

   = 103 Ncm

   R$_C$ = 103 ÷ 100 = 1.03 N

   To find R$_D$: CWM = ACWM about point C

   R$_D$ × 100 = 0.2 × 20 + 1.2 × 50 + 0.9 × 70

   = 127 Ncm

   R$_D$ = 127 ÷ 100 = 1.27 N

R$_C$ + R$_D$ = 1.03 + 1.27 = 2.3 N

= sum of downward forces = 0.2 + 1.2 + 0.9 = 2.3 N

3. The weight of the wheel W, acts vertically downward from the centre of gravity, X. The wheel is in contact with the kerb at E, so there is a normal reaction force R at this point. The wheel is just on the point of moving over the kerb, so it is in equilibrium. This means that the three forces acting on the wheel, the weight, the pulling force of 240 N and the normal force from E must act through the same point. This point is the axle of the wheel, X. Taking moments about the point E means that we ignore the reaction force R as it does not have a moment about this point.

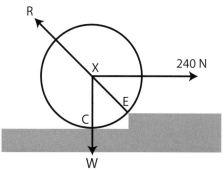

The perpendicular distance from E to the 240 N force is 0.3 m.

The perpendicular distance from E to the line of action of the weight W is 0.4 m (by Pythagoras).

Taking moments about E: 240 × 0.3 = W × 0.4

giving W = 180 N

4. (a) The weight of the **diver** and the perpendicular distance from diver to pivot.

   (b) (i) Maximum moment = Weight of diver × maximum distance from diver to pivot.

   Maximum distance to pivot = (4.88 – 1.60) + 0.28 = 3.56 m

   Maximum moment = Fd = 65 × 9.81 × 3.56 = 2270 Nm

   (ii) Moment = Weight of diver × distance from diver to pivot

   2270 = 75 × 9.81 × d = 735.75 d

   d = 2270 ÷735.75 = 3.09 m

   Distance from diver to central position = 4.88 – 1.60 = 3.28 m

   Pivot must move 3.28 – 3.09 = 0.19 m to the right

5. (a) See text.

   (b) (i) For equilibrium of vertical forces an upward force of 175 – 50 = 125 N acts at wheel.

   (ii) Let horizontal distance from centre of gravity to the centre of the wheel be d.

   ACWM = CWM about centre of wheel

   50 × 1.4 = 175 × d

   d = 70 ÷ 175 = 0.40 m

   So distance from centre of gravity to end of handle

   = 1.40 – 0.40 = 1.00 m

6. (a) Take moments about left support:

   30 × 1 = 18 × 0.5 + F$_Y$ × 1.5 giving F$_Y$ = 14 N

   Take moments about right support:

   30 × 0.5 + 18 × 2.0 = F$_X$ × 1.5 giving F$_X$ = 34 N

   (b) Take moments about left support, and let weight at left end be F and set F$_Y$ = 0:

   F × 0.5 = 30 × 1, giving F = 60 N , so weight must be increased by (60 – 18) = 42 N

Exercise 8 – *Unit 1.7*

1. Additional force to be overcome due to hill
   $= mg \sin \theta = 1200 \times g \times \sin 5.7° = 1169.19$ N
   Additional power required
   $= Fv = 1169.19 \times 30 = 35\ 076$ W ≈ 35 kW
   Total power required $= 60 + 35 = 95$ kW (to 2 sf)

2. $P = Fv$, so $2400 = 8000 \times v$
   $v = 0.3$ ms^{-1}

3. (a) Kinetic energy: energy possessed by body because of its motion.
   Potential energy: energy possessed by body because of its height above the   ground.
   (b) Straight line graph through (0,3) and (3,0). Energy conservation applied because the total energy at all points on the graph $(E_k + E_p) = 3$ J.
   (c) (i) Total energy $= mg\Delta h + \frac{1}{2}mv^2$
       $= 75 \times 9.81 \times 1.60 + 0.5 \times 75 \times 0.80^2 = 1200$ J (to 2 sf)
   (ii) $E_{total} = \frac{1}{2}mv^2 = 0.5 \times 75 \times v^2 = 1200$
       $v = \sqrt{1200 \div 37.5} = 5.7$ ms^{-1} (to 2 sf)

4. (a) useful output power = efficiency × total input power
       $= 0.04 \times 60 = 2.4$ W
   (b) efficiency $= \dfrac{\text{useful power output}}{\text{total power input}} = \dfrac{2.4}{12} = 0.2 = 20\%$

5. (a) Work done per second = Power = Fv
       $= 50\ 000 \times 30 = 1\ 500\ 000$ W $= 1.5$ MW
       So train does 1.5 MJ every second
   (b) $P = kv^3$, so $1.5 \times 10^6 = k \times 30^3$ giving $k = 55.556$
       At 40 ms^{-1}, $P = 56.5556 \times 40^3 = 3.56$ MW ≈ 3.6 MW (to 2 sf)

6. (i) KE at bottom $= 0.85 \times$ GPE at top
       $= 0.85 \times (90 \times 9.81 \times 8) = 6004$ J
       KE $= \frac{1}{2}v^2 = 6004 = \frac{1}{2} \times 90 \times v^2$ so
       $v = \sqrt{6004 \div 45} = 11.55 \approx 12$ ms^{-1} (to 2 sf)
   (ii) KE at top of second hill $= \frac{1}{2}mv^2 = \frac{1}{2} \times 90 \times 8.9^2 = 3564.5$ J
       Change in PE going up second hill $= mg\Delta h =$
       $90 \times 9.81 \times 6 = 5297$ J
       Work done $= (PE + KE)_{\text{at top}} - KE_{\text{at bottom}}$
       $= (5297 + 3564.5) - 6004 = 2858$ J
       Work done ≈ 2900 J (to 2 sf)

Exercise 9 – *Unit 1.8*

1. A ¼ turn reduces the length of the cube by
   $0.500 / 4 = 0.125$ mm
   Hooke's Law constant, $k = F \div x = 600$ kN $\div 0.125$ mm
   $= 4800$ kNmm$^{-1} = 4.8 \times 10^6$ Nm^{-1}

2. (i) Tension in each spring is 36 N
   (ii) Extension of first spring $= F \div k = 36 \div 12 = 3$ cm
       Extension of second spring $= F \div k = 36 \div 18 = 2$ cm
       Total extension $= 3 + 2 = 5$ cm
       Hooke's Law constant for combination $=$
       $F \div x = 36 \div 5 = 7.2$ Ncm^{-1}

3. (a) See text
   (b) Additional 4 N stretches the spring 6 cm.
       So $k = 4$ N $\div 6$ cm $= 0.67$ Ncm^{-1}

Exercise 10 – *Unit 1.8*

1. (a) $E = \sigma \div \varepsilon = (F \div A) \div (\varepsilon \div L) = FL \div A\varepsilon$
   (b) See text

2. (a)

Mass added / kg	Load / N	Length of spring / cm	Extension / cm	Load ÷ Extension / Ncm^{-1}
1	9.8	6.1	0.9	10.9
2	19.6	7.0	1.8	10.9
3	29.4	7.9	2.7	10.9
4	39.2	8.8	3.6	10.9
5	49.1	9.7	4.5	10.9

The spring constant, k, is the ratio of the load to the extension within the elastic limit. From the table the values of load ÷ extension are constant for all values of load. This proves that the load is directly proportional to the extension.
The spring constant $k = 10.9$ Ncm$^{-1} = 1090$ Nm^{-1}

(b) Plot a graph of load, F, on y axis against extension, x, on x-axis. The gradient of this graph is the spring constant, k.

3. (a) See text
   (b) (i) Extension, ΔL = strain × original length
       $= 7.8 \times 10^{-4} \times 2.5 = 1.95 \times 10^{-3}$ m $= 1.95$ mm
   (ii) Rearranging $E = (F \div A) \div (\Delta L \div L_o)$ gives
       $A = (F \div E) \div (\Delta L \div L_o) = (5.5 \div 1.2 \times 10^{11}) \div (7.8 \times 10^{-4})$
       $= 5.88 \times 10^{-8}$ m$^2 = 5.88 \times 10^{-2}$ mm^2

Exercise 11 – *Unit 1.9*

1. (a) (i) $\Delta Q = I \times \Delta t = 0.4 \times (3 \times 60 \times 60) = 4320$ C
   (ii) Number of electrons = total charge ÷ charge on
       1 electron $= 4320 \div 1.6 \times 10^{-19} = 2.7 \times 10^{22}$

   (b) At the **instant the potential difference is applied**, all the free electrons acquire a drift speed at all points in the conducting cable.

2. (a) An electric current is the electric charge passing a fixed point in one second.
   (b) $I = \Delta Q \div \Delta t = (5 \times 10^{20} \times 1.6 \times 10^{-19}) \div 25 = 3.2$ A
   (c) (i) $v = s \div t$, so $t = s \div v = 0.45 \div 8 \times 10^6 = 5.625 \times 10^{-8}$ s
       (ii) $Q = It = 1.85 \times 10^{-3} \times 5.625 \times 10^8 = 1.04 \times 10^{-10}$ C
       Number of electrons = total charge ÷ charge on
       1 electron $= 1.04 \times 10^{-10} \div 1.6 \times 10^{-19} = 6.5 \times 10^8$

Exercise 12 – *Unit 1.10*

1. E.m.f. is the potential difference across the output terminals of the source when no current is being drawn from it.
   Terminal potential difference is the voltage across the terminals when a current is being drawn from the source.

2. Charge $Q = It = 1 \times 20 \times 3600 = 72\ 000$ C $= \textbf{72 kC}$
   Energy $= QV = 72\ 000 \times 12 = 864\ 000$ J $= \textbf{864 kJ}$

Exercise 13 – *Unit 1.11*

1. (a) (i) 18 Ω are in parallel with 6 Ω to give a total resistance of $(18 \times 6) \div (18 + 6) = 4.5$ Ω
   (ii) $I_1 = I_2 + I_3$
   (iii) The p.d. across the network $= IR = 6 \times 4.5 = 27$ V
       = p.d. between X and Y
       $I_3 = V \div R = 27 \div 6 = 4.5$ A

   (b) Since the pd across the network is 10 V and all resistors are identical, opposite ends of the meter are at the same potential of 5 V. So there is no potential difference across the ammeter, so no current flows in the ammeter.

2. (a) First parallel network has resistance
$(20 \times 60) \div (20 + 60) = 15\,\Omega$
Second parallel network has resistance
$(24 \times 48) \div (24 + 48) = 16\,\Omega$
Total resistance between A and B = 15 + 16 = 31 Ω
(b) $R_{circuit} = V_{battery} \div I_{battery} = 12 \div 0.3 = 40\,\Omega$
(c) So resistor R has resistance 40 – 31 = 9 Ω
(d) Voltage across second parallel combination =
$IR = 0.3 \times 16 = 4.8\,V$
Current in 48 Ω resistor = V ÷ R = 4.8 ÷ 48 = 0.1 A = 100 mA

Exercise 14 – *Unit 1.11*

1. (a) The electrical resistivity of a material is defined as numerically equal to the resistance of a sample of the material 1 m long and of cross sectional area 1 m^2.

(b)(i) $\rho = RA \div L = 9.0 \times \pi \times (1 \times 10^{-4})^2 \div 15$
$= 1.88 \times 10^{-8}\,\Omega m$

(ii) Since the wire in the coils have the same length and cross section area, the difference in their resistance depends only on their resistivity. Hence the resistance of the wire in coil B is 30 times that of the wire in coil A. So the resistance of the wire in coil B is 30 × 9 = 270 Ω.

(c)(i) For the heating element use wire from coil B. To repair the electrical connection use wire from coil A.
(ii) From Joule's Law: P = I^{2}R
We generally require a connection not to become hot, so we use a wire of minimum resistance (coil A). But a heater is designed to produce heat and hence it requires a wire of greater resistance (coil B)

2. (a) R = V ÷ I = 0.12 ÷ 3.5 = 0.034 Ω
$\rho = RA \div L = 0.034 \times \pi(0.56 \times 10^{-3})^2 \div 2 = 1.67 \times 10^{-8}\,\Omega m$

(b) Length and material are unchanged, but the radius is halved.
So the area is decreased by a factor of 4 (since A = πr^2).
So resistance increases by a factor of 4 (since R = ρL ÷ A)
Resistivity does not change because resistivity is property of material, not the wire.

Exercise 15 – *Unit 1.11*

1. (a) The pd across the terminals of the source falls as increasing current is drawn from it, resulting in energy being dissipated as heat in the source of the e.m.f.

(b) (i) The gradient of the graph is –r, where r is the internal resistance of the cell
(ii) Extrapolate the graph to where it cuts the vertical axis. The y-intercept is the e.m.f.

(c) E = V + Ir and E = 10 volts (terminal p.d. when no current is drawn)
I = V ÷ R = 9.5 ÷ 2 = 4.75 A
10 = 9.5 + 4.75r
r = 0.5 ÷ 4.75 = 0.1 Ω

2. (a) The electromotive force (e.m.f.) of a battery is defined as the energy converted into electrical energy when unit charge (1 C) passes through it.

(b) (i) Internal resistance is the opposition to current flow through the electrical power source due to the resistance of components in source (or resistance of chemicals in battery).
(ii) See text (and refer also to part (b) the question above)

Exercise 16 – *Unit 1.12*

1. (a)(i) Resistance = V ÷ I = 14.2 ÷ 8.4 = 1.69 Ω
(ii) Power = V × I = 14.2 × 8.4 = 119 W

(b)(i) The total resistance of N equal resistors R, arranged in parallel, is R ÷ N
Resistance of 1 strip = R × N = 1.69 × 6 = 10.1 Ω

(c) If one strip open circuited, the whole heating element would fail and supply no heat. A parallel arrangement means there is less current in each strip; a series arrangement would require a higher voltage source to deliver the same current to each strip as the parallel arrangement.

2. (i) Going clockwise from X to Y we have two 6 Ω resistors in series giving 12 Ω. Going anticlockwise from X to Y we also have two 6 Ω resistors in series giving 12 Ω. There are therefore two 12 Ω resistors in parallel, giving a total of 12÷2 = 6 Ω.

(ii) Going clockwise from X to Y we have two 6 Ω resistors in series giving 12 Ω. In parallel with this 12 Ω there is now an additional 6 Ω resistor, giving a combined resistance of $(6 \times 12) \div (6 + 12) = 4\,\Omega$
This 4 Ω is in series with the 6 Ω connecting Y to Z to give 10 Ω.
The 10 Ω is in parallel with the 6 Ω between X and Z, giving a total resistance of
$(6 \times 10) \div (6 + 10) = 60 \div 16 = 3.75\,\Omega$

Exercise 17 – *Unit 1.12*

1. (i) I = V÷R = 18 ÷ 720 = 0.025 A = 25 mA
(ii) V = IR = 0.025 × 120 = 3 V
(iii) Resistance between C and D = 60 + 360 = 420 Ω
$V_{OUT} = V_{CD} = \frac{R_1}{R_1 + R_2} \times V_{IN} = \frac{420}{720} \times 18 = 10.5\,V$

(iv) Resistance between C and D is a parallel combination of 420 Ω and 210 Ω. Resistance between C and D
$= (420 \times 210) \div (420 + 210) = 140\,\Omega.$
$V_{OUT} = V_{CD} = \frac{R_1}{R_1 + R_2} \times V_{IN} = \frac{140}{(240 + 60 + 140)} \times 18 = 5.73\,V$

2. (a)(i) In bright light the LDR has a resistance of 500 Ω. So $R_1 = 500\,\Omega$.
$V_{OUT} = \frac{R_1}{R_1 + R_2} \times V_{IN} = \frac{500}{(500 + 10000)} \times 12 = 0.57\,V$

(ii) In the dark, the LDR has a resistance of 100 000 Ω. So $R_1 = 200\,000\,\Omega$.
$V_{OUT} = \frac{R_1}{R_1 + R_2} \times V_{IN} = \frac{200000}{(200000 + 10000)} \times 12 = 11.43\,V$
Since $V_{out} > 10\,V$, the lamp will light (in the dark).

(b) If the positions of the LDR and the fixed resistor are swapped, and the output p.d. is now across the fixed resistor, then:

In the dark:
$V_{OUT} = \frac{R_1}{R_1 + R_2} \times V_{IN} = \frac{10000}{(200000 + 10000)} \times 12 = 0.57\,V$ and
the lamp will be OFF.

In bright light:

$$V_{OUT} = \frac{R_1}{R_1 + R_2} \times V_{IN} = \frac{10000}{(500 + 10000)} \times 12 = 11.42\,V \text{ and}$$

the lamp will be ON.

The automatic light will work in reverse, lighting up when bright and going off when dark.

Exercise 18 – Unit 2.1

1. (a) (i) The vibration of the electric or the magnetic field occurs in only one plane.When dealing with vision it is the vibrations of the electric field that are polarised but when dealing with communications e.g. TV signals it is the vibrations of the magnetic field that are are polarised.
   (ii) Look into the beam through a polarising filter. When you rotate the filter the intensity of the transmitted light should fall and then rise. The maxima and minima of the light should be separated by 90°.
   (iii) The vibrations of the particles through which the sound is passing are parallel to the direction of propagation of the sound wave.
   (b) This involves using the wave equation $v = f\lambda$.
   First the speed of the wave needs to be calculated.
   Speed = distance ÷ time = 170 ÷ 0.510 = 333 ms⁻¹.
   $\lambda = v \div f = 333 \div 512 = 0.65$ m

2. (i) The particle's displacement is perpendicular to the velocity of the wave. This means it is a transverse wave that it being propagated along the string.

   (ii) The amplitude equals the magnitude of the maximum displacement. Reading this from the graph gives a value of 0.6 mm.
   (iii) The period of the wave is the time that it takes for a complete oscillation of the particle. Reading this from the graph gives a value of 0.005 s.
   The frequency = 1 ÷ period = 1 ÷ 0.005 = 200 Hz.
   (iv) Use the wave equation $v = f\lambda$, substitution of values gives 890 = 200 × λ, giving a wavelength of 4.45 mm.
   (v) A complete cycle of the wave takes 6 of the major divisions on the graph. The point A is 2 of these divisions along the wave from the origin S, this represents ⅓ of a wave. The phase difference is therefore 360° ÷ 3 = 120° or 2π÷3 radians.

3. (a) Firstly these graphs can be used to represent the particle oscillation for either a transverse wave or a longitudinal wave. This type of graph will not tell what type of wave it. The amplitude (maximum displacement) shown on each graph is the same, 0.016 m is 1.6 cm.
   (b) (i) Figure 2 show two complete waves in a distance of 2.4 m. The wavelength is therefore 1.2 m
   (ii) Figure 1 shows 5 complete waves (cycles) in 0.036 s.
      This gives a period of 0.036÷5 = 0.0072 s
      The frequency = 1÷period = 1÷0.0072 = 139 Hz
   (iii) Use the wave equation $v = f\lambda$.
      Speed = 139 × 1.2 = 167 ms⁻¹.

Exercise 19 – Unit 2.2

1. Tabulate corresponding values of sin i and sin r.
   i = angle of incidence and r = angle of refraction.
   Plot a graph of sin i (y-axis) against sin r (x-axis).

Determine the gradient of the best fit straight line.
The gradient = sin i ÷ sin r = refractive index.

2. (a) Meeting the glass-air boundary at the critical means that the ray of light travelling from the glass into the air will be refracted into the air at an angle of 90° to the normal. This means it will travel along the glass-air boundary.
   (b) If the angle was greater than the critical angle the ray of light would undergo total internal reflection. It will be reflected back into glass with the angle of reflection being the same as the angle of incidence.
   (c) sin C = 1/refractive index = 1÷1.39 = 0.7194. C = 46°.
   (d) Look at the angles on the diagram:

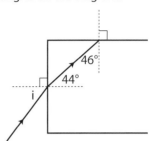

   n = sin i ÷ sin r
   1.39 = sin i ÷ sin 44
   sin i = 1.39 × 0.6947 = 0.9656
   i = 74.9°

3. The diagram shows the ray of light.

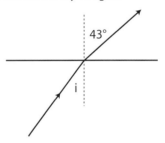

   Use Snell's law to calculate i
   sin i ÷ sin 43 = 1 ÷ 1.38 = 0.725.

   Remember the light is moving from glass into air so $_{glass}n_{air}$ = 1 ÷ $_{air}n_{glass}$
   sin i = 0.4944 giving i = 29.6°.
   To undergo total internal the angle i must just exceed the critical angle C.

   To calculate C we use sin C = 1÷1.38 = 0.725 giving a value for C = 46.5°.
   The required increase in the value of the angle i is 46.5° − 29.6° = 16.9°.

4. (a) Speed = distance÷time = 1200 m ÷ 5880 × 10⁻⁹
   = 2.04 × 10⁸ ms⁻¹.
   (b) Refractive index of a material = velocity of light in vacuum ÷ velocity of light in the material.
   The velocity of light in a vacuum (data sheet)
   = 3.0 × 10⁸ ms⁻¹.
   Refractive index = 3 × 10⁸ ÷ 2.04 × 10⁸ = 1.47
   (c) sin C = 1÷1.47 = 0.6803 giving C = 42.9°.

5. (a) sin 45°÷Sin r = 1.52 giving r = 27.7°.
   (b) Use the hint given r = 60° − 27.7° = 32.3°.
   (c) The critical angle for the material of the prism is found by: sin C = 1÷1.52 = 0.6579, C = 41.1°

The angle of incidence in the glass, namely the angle r, is only 27.7°, this is less than the critical angle so total internal reflection does not happen.

(d) sin 27.7° ÷ sin θ = 1 ÷ 1.52

(the light is travelling from glass to air - see solution to question 3)

sin θ = 0.7066, give a value for θ = 45°.

Exercise 20 – *Unit 2.3*

1. The lens shown is a diverging or concave lens.

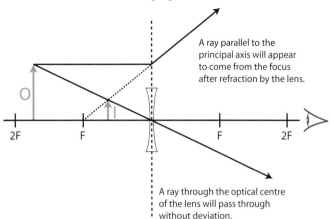

A ray parallel to the principal axis will appear to come from the focus after refraction by the lens.

A ray through the optical centre of the lens will pass through without deviation.

2. (a) The diagram of the apparatus.

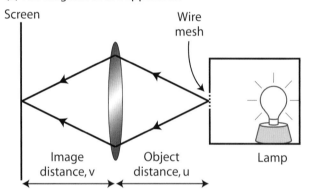

(b) Place the lens between the lamp house and the screen. Adjust the position of the screen until a sharp image is seen on the screen.

(c) Measure the distance from the lens to the wire mesh (object distance u). Measure the distance from the lens to the screen (image distance v). Repeat this process for five or six different object distances.

(d) Plot a graph of 1/u against 1/v. Draw the best fit line through the points. Extend the line until it cuts both axes. The intercepts on each axes is equal to 1/f, f is the focal length. Take an average value of 1/f and calculate f. (see the graph under 'Measuring Object and Image Distances' in text).

3. (a) The magnification, m = v÷u = 6. Thus v = 6u.

Use the lens formula $\frac{1}{u}+\frac{1}{v}=\frac{1}{f}$

Since the image is virtual the image distance is negative:

$\frac{1}{u}-\frac{1}{6u}=\frac{1}{10}$ giving $\frac{(6-1)}{6u}=\frac{1}{10}$, so $\frac{6u}{5}=10$

Thus u = 8.33 cm

(b) The image distance v = 6u = 6 × 8.33 = 50 cm.

Exercise 21 – *Unit 2.3*

1. (a) The lens is converging and is used to correct long sight or hypermetropia.

(b) (i) Power = 1÷focal length.

It is necessary to calculate the focal length in metres.

u = 0.32 m and since magnification = 2.7 = v÷u, v = 0.86 m

Using the lens formula and remembering that we are dealing with a virtual image (ie, the sign is negative for the image distance) we have:

$\frac{1}{u}+\frac{1}{v}=\frac{1}{f}$ $\frac{1}{0.32}-\frac{1}{0.86}=\frac{1}{f}$ so

$\frac{1}{f}=3.125-1.163=1.96\,\text{m}^{-1}$ or dioptre

(ii) When using this lens to correct for long sight the lens produces a virtual image at the person's defective near point of an object placed 25 cm from the eye. Using the lens formula

$\frac{1}{u}+\frac{1}{v}=\frac{1}{f}$ we have $\frac{1}{0.25}-\frac{1}{v}=1.96$ so

$\frac{1}{v}=4.0-1.96=2.04$ giving v = 0.49 m or 49 cm

2. The defect is known as short sight or myopia. A diverging (concave) lens is used to correct the defect.

Exercise 22 – *Unit 2.4*

1. (a) The light waves from the two slits are in phase or have a constant phase difference between them.

(b) In phase means that the crest of a light wave passes through slit S at the same time as a crest passes through slit T.

(c) A bright fringe is due to constructive interference between the light waves from S and T. A crest of a light wave from S meets a crest of a light wave from T. The light reaching the point on the screen has travelled different distances from the double slit. To have constructive interference the difference between these two distances, known as the path difference, is equal to a whole number of wavelengths of the light used.

(d) The fringe separation y = 24.3÷6 = 4.05 mm. Remember to count the gaps not the number of fringes. The slit separation a = 0.66 mm and the wavelength λ = 6.42 × 10⁻⁷ m.

$\lambda=\frac{ay}{d}$ re-arranged gives $d=\frac{ay}{\lambda}$

convert all distances to metres

$d=\frac{0.66\times10^{-3}\times4.05\times10^{-3}}{6.42\times10^{-7}}=4.16\,\text{m}$

2. The distance from the central bright fringe to the next one is the fringe separation y. This is calculated as below:

$\lambda=\frac{ay}{d}$ re-arranged gives $d=\frac{ay}{\lambda}$

convert all distances to metres

$d=\frac{550\times10^{-9}\times1.80}{0.91\times10^{-3}}=1.09\times10^{-3}\,\text{m}\ \ (1.09\,\text{mm})$

3. (a) Interference is the phenomenon in which two waves superpose each other to form a resultant wave of greater or lower amplitude.

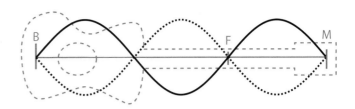

(b) The waves must be of the same type e.g. two sound waves, two water waves or two light waves or two waves on a string. They must have the same wavelength. They must be coherent, ie in phase, or have a constant phase difference between them.

(c) To produce good contrast between the bright and dark fringes requires the two wave to have the same amplitude, ie brightness.

Exercise 23 – *Unit 2.4*

1. (a) This is the third mode of vibration. A quick way to work this out is to count the loops.

(b) An antinode is where the displacement of the string reaches a maximum. The diagram shows the three possible antinodes that you could mark.

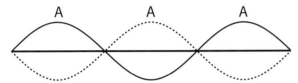

(c) The distance between consecutive antinodes is ½λ. ½λ = 0.08 so λ = 0.16 m.

(d) The fundamental mode of vibration consists of a single loop as shown below.

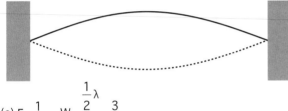

(e) $F = \dfrac{1}{3}$ $W = \dfrac{\dfrac{1}{2}\lambda}{\dfrac{2}{3}\lambda} = \dfrac{3}{4}$

2. (a) (i) and (ii)

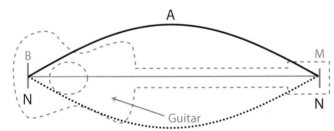

(b) (i) For the first mode of vibration the length of string is ½ λ. The wavelength λ is therefore 1.68 m.

(ii) A frequency of 328 Hz is 4 times the lowest frequency of 82 Hz.

The new wavelength will therefore be ¼ of 1.68 m = 0.42 m.

The length of string BX will be ½ of this and equal to 0.21 m.

(c) The point F is ⅔ of the way along the string, there will be a node at this point as well as nodes at B and M.

Exercise 24 – *Unit 2.5*

1. (a) Diffraction is the spreading out of waves as they through small openings or around small obstacles.

(b) The gap is much greater than the wavelength so the amount of diffraction will be small and only occur at the edges of the wavefronts as shown. The wavefronts should be drawn linear with curved ends and spreading out. Make sure the wavelength is kept constant.

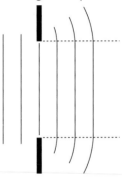

(c) The wavelength of speech (approximately 1 m) is similar to the dimensions of the door so appreciable diffraction occurs. The wavelength of light (around 500 nm) is very small so only occurs with very narrow gaps.

2. (a) The size of the gap is nearly the same as the wavelength of waves so the amount of diffraction will be much greater than that shown in question 1.

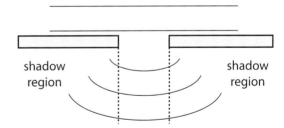

(b) As the wavelength of the sound increases the amount of diffraction will increase and the sound will spread more into the shadow zone. This means the shadow zone will get smaller.

Exercise 25 – *Unit 2.6*

1. 2 ½ waves are shown. The time for these is
5.6 cm × 2.00 ms cm^{-1} μ = 11.2 ms
The period of 1 wave T = 11.2÷2.5 = 4.48 ms
The frequency f = 1÷T = 1 ÷ 48 × 10^{-3} = 223 Hz.

2. (a)

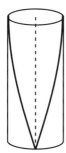

(b) The sound becomes much louder at the resonance position.

(c) $L = \frac{1}{4}\lambda$.

(d) $v = f\lambda$, $f = \frac{v}{\lambda} = \frac{v}{4L}$ so $\frac{1}{f} = \frac{4L}{v}$

3. (a) To 3 significant figures the values are 3.21, 3.61, 3.88, 5.29, 6.02

(c) The gradient of the best fit line through the origin is 84.0.
The unit is $s^{-1}m$ or simply ms^{-1}

(d) $f = \frac{v}{\lambda} = \frac{v}{4L}$ so the gradient is $\frac{v}{4}$

So the speed of sound is $4 \times$ gradient $= 4 \times 84 = 336\ ms^{-1}$

4. (a) (i) The sound wave travels from the speaker to the closed end where it is reflected back up the tube interference then results between these two waves.

(ii) $\lambda = v \div f = 340 \div 304 = 1.12\ m$

(iii) The standing patterns form a sequence.
The length of the air column is $\frac{1}{4}\lambda$, $\frac{3}{4}\lambda$, $\frac{5}{4}\lambda$.
A wavelength of 1.12 m corresponds to $1.40 \div 1.12 = 1.25$
The standing wave will wave a node at the closed end and three antinodes, one of them at the open end:

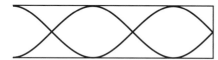

(b) The minimum frequency is for the fundamental mode, where $\lambda = 4L$
$v = f\lambda$ so $f = v \div \lambda = 965 \div (4 \times 1.40) = 965 \div 5.60 \approx 172\ Hz$

Exercise 26 – Unit 2.6

1. (a) A logarithmic scale
(b) (i) Similarity – dogs and humans have the same lower frequency limit namely 20Hz. Difference – the upper limit for dogs at 50kHz is much greater than the upper limit for humans of 20kHz. A wider range of frequency is another acceptable answer.
(ii) The minimum should occur at –20 dB and 5000 Hz. The left hand side of the curve should be the same as that for human but the right hand side should extend to 50 kHz.
(iii) The dog would hear a much louder sound as the intensity level for a dog at this frequency is much lower than for humans –20 dB as opposed to approximately +10dB.

Exercise 27 – Unit 2.7

1. (a) Field gradient coils – there are three such coils which surround the patient. They are used to produce changes in the steady magnetic field which allows the location of the emitted radio signals from the patient to be located.

The computer – this processes the radio frequency signals to produce an image.
(b) The magnetic field is produced using an electromagnet. The use of superconducting materials allows a very large current to be used without heating loss due to resistance.
(c) Advantages of MRI compared to CT scanning include: no ionising X-rays are used; an image from any plane can be produced; greater detail is visible especially in soft tissue.

2. (a) As the ultrasound passes through the tissue of the body some of it is absorbed so there is less energy to reflect back to the transducer.
(b) The time delay between the outgoing pulse and its reflection is 8 cm × 1 μs/cm = 8 μs (8×10^{-6} s).
This represents a round trip distance of $8 \times 10^{-6} \times 4 \times 10^{3}$
$= 0.032\ m = 32\ mm$
Divide this by 2 to get a bone thickness of 16 mm.

3. (a) A tomograph is detailed image of the structure of an object (body) through one plane. This can be achieved by using X-rays or MRI scanning. The term is derived from the Greek word *tomos* which means "part" or "section", representing the idea of a section, or a slice. A tomograph of several sections of the body is known as a polytomograph. *Poly* is a Greek word meaning many.
(b) The two mechanisms in the production of X-rays are braking radiation which accounts for the continuous range of X-ray wavelengths produced and the second is the ejection of the electrons from the atoms of the target material this produces the emission line spectrum of the X-rays. See the section on X-ray production for more detail.
(c) (i) The 99% energy loss is in the form of heat. The kinetic energy of the high speed electrons is converted to vibrational energy (heat) of the atoms of the target material. The target material (tungsten) is embedded in a copper anode, a very good heat conductor. The anode spins so distributing the heat around the anode. The heat is transferred to the metal parts of the assembly which lose heat by radiation. Oil circulating around the X-ray tube removes some the unwanted heat by convection.
(ii) The X-rays produced have a range of wavelengths. Those of long wavelength (low energy) are known as soft X-rays and are of little use in producing an X-ray image. However they do add to the radiation dose the patient receives. They are removed by the aluminium filter, which absorbs them.

Exercise 28 – Unit 2.8

1. (a) A photon is a quantum of electromagnetic energy.
(b) $E = hf = 6.63 \times 10^{-34} \times 6.00 \times 10^{16} = 3.98 \times 10^{-17}$ J.
(c) Emission of an electron from a metal due to the absorption of electromagnetic radiation and it happens when photon energy is greater than the metal's work function.

2. (a) The gradient = frequency÷energy or = f÷E.
The Planck relationship gives E = hf
so the gradient = 1÷h = 1÷6.63 × 10⁻³⁴ Js
$= 1.51 \times 10^{33}\ J^{-1}s^{-1}$
(b) $E = hf = 6.63 \times 10^{-34} \times 200 \times 10^{6} = 1.33 \times 10^{-25}$ J
or using $E = hc \div \lambda = 6.63 \times 10^{-34} \times 3 \times 10^{8} \div 1.5$
$= 1.33 \times 10^{-25}$ J

3. (a) The work function is the minimum energy required to eject an electron from the surface of the metal.
(b) $1eV = 1.6 \times 10^{-19}$ J
so the work function $= 1.85 \times 1.6 \times 10^{-19} = 2.96 \times 10^{-19}$ J
(c) $E = hf$ so $2.96 \times 10^{-19} = 6.63 \times 10^{-34} \times f$
$f = 4.46 \times 10^{14}$ Hz.

4. (a) (i) $E = hc \div \lambda = 6.63 \times 10^{-34} \times 3 \times 10^{8} \div 290 \times 10^{-9}$
$= 6.86 \times 10^{-19}$ J
(ii) Energy delivered to surface $= 1.6 \times 10^{-4} \times 0.034$
$= 5.44 \times 10^{-6}$ J
Each photon delivers an energy of 6.86×10^{-19} J
The number of photons per second
$= 5.44 \times 10^{-6} \div 6.86 \times 10^{-19} = 7.93 \times 10^{12}$

(b) (i) An increase in the intensity means more photons per second strike the metal so more electrons per second are ejected from the metal.
(ii) Increasing the intensity has no effect on the maximum kinetic energy of the ejected electrons. Remember the energy of the photon depends only on its frequency or wavelength.

Exercise 29 – Unit 2.9

1. (a) Quantised means that the energy levels have a well defined or very specific value.
(b) (i) The minimum value of intensity occurs at a frequency of 6.13×10^{14} Hz
Use of $E=hf$ gives 4.06×10^{-19} J
(ii) The above energy when converted to electron volts gives 2.54 eV
The correct transition is from 3.39 eV to 0.85 eV
The light is being absorbed so the photons causes the electrons to move from lower energy to higher energy in this case from – 3.39 eV to – 0.85 eV.

2. (a) A quantum of energy 200 eV is sufficient to remove the electron from the atom, ionisation occurs.
(b) Nothing happens since 5.7 eV does not correspond to the difference between any of the energy levels.
(c) The energy of this photon is 163.3 eV and is hence due to an electron dropping from the –54.4 eV level to the –217.7eV level.

Exercise 30 – Unit 2.9

1. (a) (i) A lot more electrons are present in the excited state than the ground state. (ii) This is known as a population inversion. Remember the ground state normally has a lot more electrons than any excited state.
(iii) The presence of a photon produced from a spontaneous transition of an electron from the excited state to the ground stimulates many of the electrons in the excited to make the transition to the ground state.

Exercise 31 – Unit 2.10

1. (a) λ is the de broglie wavelength associated with a moving particle.
h = Planck's constant and p = momentum of the moving particle.
(b) Re–arranging the equation gives $1 \div p = \lambda \div h$.
The gradient is therefore $1 \div h = 1 \div 6.63 \times 10^{-34}$ Js
$= 1.51 \times 10^{33}$ J^{-1}s^{-1}.

2. (a) (i) Polarisation is a phenomenon associated only with waves so the wave model is appropriate. The photoelectric effect is explained using the idea of a quantum or discrete amount of electromagnetic energy so the particle model is appropriate in this case.
(ii) Reflection and refraction can be explained using either model.
(b) Use the relationship $\lambda = h \div p$
$= 6.63 \times 10^{-34} \div (6.64 \times 10^{-27} \times 4.5 \times 10^{6}) = 2.21 \times 10^{-14}$ m.
Note that the charge is a piece of data not required in this calculation.

3. (a) Electrons are accelerated to high speed and allowed to pass through a thin sheet of graphite (carbon atoms). The electrons are diffracted by the carbon atoms and when they reach a fluorescent screen a series of alternate bright and dark rings are seen. This is an interference pattern typical of waves. See the section on electron diffraction.
(b) A smaller velocity means the electrons have less momentum and so applying the de broglie relationship tells us that the associated wavelength is larger so the spacing between rings of the electron diffraction pattern increases.